BrightRED Study Guide

CfE HIGHER

HUMAN BIOLOGY

Cara Matthew, Angela Grant and Kathleen Ritchie

First published in 2015 by:
Bright Red Publishing Ltd
1 Torphichen Street
Edinburgh
EH3 8HX

Reprinted with corrections in 2016 and 2018

New edition published 2019

A CIP record for this book is available from the British Library.

ISBN 978-1-84948-327-8

With thanks to:
PDQ Digital Media Solutions Ltd, Bungay (layout), Anna Stevenson (copy-edit).

Cover design and series book design by Caleb Rutherford – e i d e t i c.

Acknowledgements
Every effort has been made to seek all copyright holders. If any have been overlooked, then Bright Red Publishing will be delighted to make the necessary arrangements.

Permission has been sought from all relevant copyright holders and Bright Red Publishing is grateful for the use of the following:

Andrea Danti/Shutterstock.com (p 11); Mike Jones (CC BY-SA 2.5)[1] (p 11); Helixitta/Creative Commons (CC BY-SA 3.0)[2] (p 17); ttsz/iStock.com (p 24); difught/iStock.com (p 35); OSTILL/iStock.com (p 35); koya79/iStock.com (p 43); Wolfgang Moroder (CC BY-SA 3.0)[2] (p 44); sportEX journals (CC BY-ND 2.0)[3]; photo5963/iStock.com (p 61); selvanegra/iStock.com (p 73); ttsz/iStock.com (pp 74 & 88); 4774344sean/iStock.com (p 75); susandaniels/iStock.com (p 75); blueringmedia/iStock.com (p 75); Suze777/iStock.com (p 76); yangna/iStock.com (p 78); Minerva Studio/iStock.com (p 83); *Question taken from Higher Human Biology Exemplar, paper 2 question 12 © Scottish Qualifications Authority (p 81) (n.b. solutions do not emanate from the SQA).*

(CC BY-SA 2.5)[1]   https://creativecommons.org/licenses/by-sa/2.5/

(CC BY-SA 3.0)[2]   http://creativecommons.org/licenses/by-sa/3.0/

(CC BY-ND 2.0)[3]   http://creativecommons.org/licenses/by-nd/2.0/

Printed and bound in the UK.

CONTENTS

INTRODUCTION

Introducing CfE Higher Human Biology 4

Revision Techniques 6

Data Handling Tips 8

HUMAN CELLS

Division and Differentiation in Human Cells 10

Stem Cells 12

The Structure of DNA 14

Polymerase Chain Reaction (PCR) 16

Gene Expression 18

Protein Synthesis 20

One Gene, Many Proteins 22

Mutations 24

Human Genomics 26

Metabolism 28

Enzyme Action 30

Cellular Respiration 32

Exercise and Energy Systems in Muscle Cells 34

Revision Questions 36

PHYSIOLOGY AND HEALTH

Male Reproductive System 38

Female Reproductive System 40

The Biology of Controlling Fertility 42

Antenatal and Postnatal Screening 44

Pedigree Charts (Family Trees) 46

Cardiovascular System 48

The Heart 50

Blood Pressure and Electrocardiograms 52

Pathology of Cardiovascular Disease (CVD) 1 54

Pathology of Cardiovascular Disease (CVD) 2 56

Blood Glucose Level and Diabetes 58

Obesity 60

Revision Questions 62

NEUROBIOLOGY AND IMMUNOLOGY

Divisions of the Nervous System 64

Memory 66

Nervous System 68

Neurotransmitters and Recreational Drugs 70

Immunology 72

Specific Cellular Defences Against Pathogens 1 74

Specific Cellular Defences Against Pathogens 2 76

Immunisation 1 78

Immunisation 2 80

Clinical Trials of Vaccines and Drugs 82

Revision Questions 84

APPENDICES

Answers 86

INDEX 91

INTRODUCTION

INTRODUCING CFE HIGHER HUMAN BIOLOGY

The CfE Higher Human Biology course is divided into three topics:

- Topic 1: Human Cells
- Topic 2: Physiology and Health
- Topic 3: Neurobiology and Immunology

COURSE ASSESSMENT

The course assessment is made up of three components with a total of 140 marks. It is graded A to D, which is determined on the basis of the total mark for all components.

Components 1 and 2: Question Papers

You will sit an externally assessed written examination consisting of two papers. Question Paper 1 has 25 multiple choice questions. It will last 40 minutes. Question Paper 2 is an extended-response paper which is worth 95 marks and has a duration of 2 hours 20 minutes. It contains restricted-response and extended-response questions. The course assessment addresses:

- Breadth – drawing on knowledge and skills from across the course.
- Challenge – requiring greater depth or extension of knowledge and/or skills.
- Application – requiring application of knowledge and/or skills in practical or theoretical contexts as appropriate.

Marks are distributed proportionally across the course content. The majority are awarded for demonstrating and applying knowledge and understanding. The other marks are awarded for applying scientific inquiry, scientific analytical thinking, problem-solving skills and knowledge of the impact of applications of biology on society and the environment.

Component 3: Assignment

The course assignment is worth 20 marks. You will investigate a relevant topic in biology that is related to one or more of the key areas in the Higher Human Biology course and then communicate your findings. This requires you to demonstrate your application of scientific-enquiry skills, and related biological knowledge and understanding.

EXAM HINTS

You do not need to answer the questions in order. At the beginning of the exam, find a question that you can answer easily, so that you settle your nerves.

Timekeeping is important, if you are to complete the whole paper. As a general rule, you should be taking just under one and a half minutes per mark.

Remember to look at the mark allocation for each question. Extended-response questions that are worth from 6 to 9 marks require more lengthy answers – remember to allocate sufficient time to these.

REVISION TIPS

- Don't leave your revision until the last minute. Make up a revision schedule, giving yourself enough time to revise thoroughly, and stick to it. Be realistic – you should work around your other activities and remember that you do need to take time off to relax.

- Find somewhere to study that is quiet and uncluttered. You need space to spread out your work.

- Study for short periods (between 30 and 45 minutes) with short breaks in between, to keep up your level of concentration. Go out of the room where you are studying during each break; you will return refreshed and ready for your next study session.

- Read over each sub-topic at a slower pace than you would usually do, asking yourself questions or reading aloud. Make sure that you understand what you have been reading – you only learn what you understand.

- It's often easier to remember facts if you talk about topics with a family member or a friend. So, find a study buddy who can ask you questions about your work.

- Practice makes perfect; do past-paper practice so that the exam format is as familiar as possible. There are only a few ways in which you can be asked the same question, and you will see similar questions and diagrams appearing in many past papers. Doing a past paper against the clock will help you to get your time management right.

- In the run up to the exams, eat plenty of fresh fruit and vegetables to keep your energy levels up, and make sure that you get a good night's sleep so that you are alert on the day of the exam.

- Switch off all mobile devices and social media.

THE STRUCTURE AND AIMS OF THIS BOOK

There is no shortcut to passing any course at Higher level. To obtain a good pass requires consistent, regular revision over the duration of the course. The aim of this revision book is to help you achieve success by providing you with a concise and engaging coverage of the CfE Higher Human Biology course material. We recommend that you use this book in conjunction with your class notes, to revise each topic area, prepare for any class assessments, to help with homework and in your preparation for the final exam.

The book is divided between the topics which make up the course. Within each section, there is a double-page spread on each of the sub-sections.

Each double-page spread:

- Provides the key ideas and concepts of the sub-section in a logical and digestible manner.

- Contains 'Internet Links' and 'Don't Forget' boxes that flag up vital pieces of knowledge that you need to remember and important things that you must be able to do.

- Gives a link to an online test to test your knowledge and understanding of each topic.

- Ends with a 'Things To Do and Think About' feature which extends your knowledge and understanding of the subject, and provides additional interest. Sometimes there are questions to help you check your understanding.

- Contains revision questions to test your knowledge and understanding of the course content.

Good luck, and enjoy!

REVISION TECHNIQUES

Many people try to revise by spending hours reading over and highlighting their notes or revision books. This often leads to a false sense of security as over time they become very familiar with the format of the information but don't necessarily understand it and may not be able to apply the knowledge. To make your revision more efficient, you should use a combination of several techniques, which will increase both long-term retention and the ability to apply knowledge to unfamiliar situations.

TECHNIQUE 1: RETRIEVAL PRACTICE

Once you have learned a topic, you must check that you know and understand it. Try the following retrieval techniques.

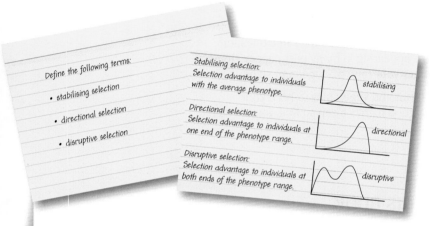

Flash Cards

The terms to be learned are written on one side of an index card and the definitions are written on the other side. You should then work through the topic flash cards, giving the definition before turning over and checking the answer. A quick line drawing (where appropriate) can help with recall (see dual coding below). Another tip is to use a parent or friend as a study buddy and ask them to run through the flash cards so that you can talk your way through the cards. Often this allows you to elaborate on the basic facts that are contained on the cards – by elaborating you enhance the memory, making it stronger.

DON'T FORGET

By elaborating and telling a more detailed story you strengthen the memory.

Mind Maps

These are diagrams which allow you to summarise the main facts within a topic, establishing links between ideas. Again, a combination of words and pictures is used. Once the mind map has been memorised, try drawing it out on a blank sheet of paper. Alternatively, talk through the mind map with your study buddy.

Writing Out Topic Facts/Talking Through Revision Notes with a Study Buddy

Try writing down all the facts you can remember about a topic on a blank sheet of paper. This can include diagrams and may be in the form of bullet points. Next, check the information that you have written against your revision notes and look for facts that you have missed. Make sure that you relearn any areas that were not correctly recalled and then test yourself again. Alternatively, learn one or two topic spreads from this revision book and then hand it to your study buddy and ask them to check that you can describe and explain the content without missing anything. Again, go back and relearn areas that you have not correctly remembered.

Past-Paper Practice

There is no point in knowing the facts if you cannot use them to answer questions. Trying as many exam-type questions as possible is absolutely key to gaining the best possible grades in the final exam. Through the year, teachers will provide relevant questions in homework and revision materials.

Several SQA past papers for each subject can be downloaded free of charge from the SQA website. Books of SQA past papers and also specially written exam-type practice question papers can be purchased from bookshops or the internet. Teachers often supply older

contd

SQA past-paper questions on request and several school websites give access to older papers (try the search term: 'old SQA higher biology past papers').

Make sure that you check the answers against the marking scheme and seek assistance if you are having difficulties by attending supported study classes or by speaking to the class teacher.

TECHNIQUE 2: SPACED PRACTICE

Revisiting topics many times over the course of a session (**spaced practice**) is a much more successful revision technique than 'cramming' in the run up to the exams. This works as a study method because in the time between revision sessions we tend to forget some information. The relearning process you then go through the next time you study the same topic actually results in a 'stronger' memory. A revision plan such as that shown below can help you keep track of your study sessions.

Metabolic pathways	Study session completed					
Metabolic pathways can have reversible steps, irreversible steps and alternative routes. Anabolic reactions build up large molecules from small molecules and require energy. Catabolic reactions break down large molecules into smaller molecules and release energy.						
Metabolic pathways are controlled by the presence or absence of particular enzymes and the regulation of the rate of reaction of key enzymes.						
Induced fit and the role of the active site of an enzyme in affecting activation energy and the affinity of the substrate and products for the active site.						
The effects of substrate concentration on the direction and rate of enzyme reactions.						
Control of metabolic pathways through competitive, non-competitive and feedback inhibition of enzymes.						

You can use spaced practice with your flash cards by setting up boxes for each day of the week. Cards that are successfully recalled on Monday could be put in a Thursday or Friday box or left in a box for the next week or fortnight. Those that were not recalled correctly should be put in the next day's box for more rapid retesting.

TECHNIQUE 3: INTERLEAVING

Interleaving involves studying more than one sub-topic or topic during a study session. This works best when the sub-topics are related as it allows you to expand on similarities and differences between the sub-topics, developing your reasoning strategies. Interleaving works well with spaced practice. An example of a revision schedule which incorporates both techniques is shown below.

Topic to be studied	REVISION DAY				
	Monday	Tuesday	Wednesday	Thursday	Friday
DNA replication	X			X	
PCR	X				X
Transcription and RNA splicing		X			X
Translation and post-translational modification		X			
Gene mutations				X	

 DON'T FORGET

It helps to remember facts if you use concrete examples whenever you can.

ONLINE

You can also visit our BrightRED Digital Zone www.brightredbooks.net for tests, videos and further reading on each topic!

TECHNIQUE 4: DUAL CODING

Dual coding is where we use a combination of words and diagrams in revision materials, giving two ways to remember the information. Flash cards and mind maps can both incorporate words and pictures, which will help you remember facts.

INTRODUCTION

DATA HANDLING TIPS

TIPS FOR DATA HANDLING

Here is an example of incorrect data handling, followed by the correct recording for the same data.

Wrong

Age	Mass
2	12.3
3	14
4	16.3

Correct

Age (years)	Mass (Kg)
2	12.3
3	14.0
4	16.3

Units should be included in the column headings and the masses should be recorded to the same number of decimal places.

Percentage Change

Some questions ask you to calculate the percentage change or percentage increase or percentage decrease.

In these instances, you should always use the same formula:

$$\% \text{ change} = \frac{\text{difference}}{\text{original number}} \times 100$$

Day	Height (cm)
1	1.2
2	2.0
3	2.3
4	2.8

Find the percentage increase in height between days 1 and 4.

Solution

Difference = height at day 4 − height at day 1

$$= 2.8 - 1.2$$

$$= 1.6 \text{ cm}$$

$$\% \text{ change} = \left(\frac{\text{difference}}{\text{original number}}\right) \times 100$$

$$\% \text{ change} = \left(\frac{1.6}{1.2}\right) \times 100$$

$$= 1.33 \times 100$$

$$= 133\% \text{ increase in height}$$

Think about it: many people think that you cannot have a percentage value greater than 100.

If you look at the height on day 4 (2.8 cm) you can see that it is **more than double** the height on day 1 (1.2 cm), so the percentage increase must be more than 100.

DON'T FORGET

Use a pencil and ruler to draw graphs, charts and tables.

EXPERIMENTAL DESIGN QUESTIONS

Variables

The Independent Variable

Only one variable should be altered for a valid experiment.

The Dependent Variable

Quite simply, this is the result of the experiment. What did you measure and record at the end of the experiment?

Controlled Variables

These are all the things that could affect the result of an experiment and therefore must be kept the same (what is the same each time?).

You should be able to identify at least three things that should be kept the same each time (there will always be more than three, so this should be straightforward). Choose the most relevant from the list below.

- the age of...
- the volume of...
- the concentration of...
- the incubation time
- the temperature
- the type of...
- the number of...
- the height, length, etc. of...
- the mass of...

The Control Experiment

This is for **comparison**. An identical experiment is set up that does not contain the independent variable. For example if you were looking at the effect of fertiliser on plant growth you would use a plant grown with fertiliser and a plant grown without fertiliser (this would be the control). This would prove that any changes that happened were due to the effect of the fertiliser and wouldn't have happened randomly.

The Evaluation

Think of the ways that you could improve your experiment, for example:

- Use a wider range of... (temperature, pH, etc.).
- Have a more precise scale.
- Use a larger sample size.

You should have repeated the experiment several times, so this is a weak answer in an evaluation.

Reliability Versus Accuracy

These terms are often mixed up. **Reliability** is achieved by **repeating** the experiment several times and calculating an average.

Reliable
e
p
e
a
t

Accuracy is achieved by using more **precise** equipment to measure. For example:

- using a balance to 2 or 3 decimal places
- using scales with more divisions, such as a measuring cylinder instead of a beaker or a pipette scale with divisions every 0.1 cm³ instead of every 1 cm³
- using mm instead of cm on a ruler
- using a pH probe instead of pH paper
- using a digital thermometer instead of a mercury thermometer.

HUMAN CELLS

DIVISION AND DIFFERENTIATION IN HUMAN CELLS

MITOSIS AND MEIOSIS

Mitosis

Mitosis has one division to separate chromosomes. The new daughter cells maintain the diploid number.

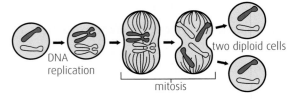

Meiosis

Meiosis has two divisions: the first meiotic division separates the homologous pairs, and the second meiotic division separates the chromatids. The separation of pairs means that the gametes produced are haploid.

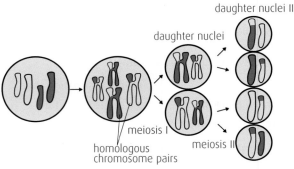

DON'T FORGET

Most diploid cells in the body, plus red blood cells, are categorised as **somatic cells**. Any cells involved with reproduction, including haploid gametes, are categorised as **germline cells**.

STEM CELLS

The somatic (body) cells increase in number by **mitosis**.

DON'T FORGET

Division by mitosis produces more germline cells. Division by meiosis produces haploid gametes (sperm and ova).

GERMLINE CELLS

Germline cells are situated in the testes and ovaries. They can replace themselves by the nucleus dividing by **mitosis** or they can produce haploid gametes by the nucleus dividing by **meiosis**.

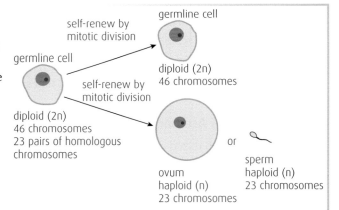

DON'T FORGET

Differentiated cells only express genes which produce proteins that are vital for survival or that are required to enable the cell to perform its specialised function.

ONLINE TEST

Want to test yourself on this topic? Head to www.brightredbooks.net

CELLULAR DIFFERENTIATION

As soon as fertilisation occurs, the **zygote** (fertilised egg) begins to divide by mitosis. It forms a ball of identical and **unspecialised** cells. Then, as the cells become specialised for specific functions, regions in the continually dividing embryo start to behave differently from each other. This is called differentiation and happens when:

- **some genes** are switched off
- genes that are vital to all living cells, for example those for respiratory enzymes, are **expressed** (transcribed)
- genes for specialised cell functions are expressed. For example, contractile proteins are synthesised in muscle, the enzymes required to make neurotransmitters are synthesised in neurons, and the digestive enzymes are synthesised in specific regions of the digestive system.

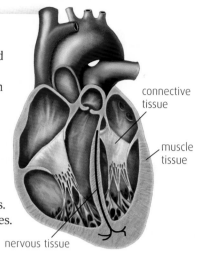

Dissected heart

connective tissue

muscle tissue

nervous tissue

STEM CELLS: AN OVERVIEW

Stem cells are unspecialised and can divide to form specialised cells. They are found in all parts of the body and can differentiate into one or a few cell types that are characteristic for their location. The degree of specialisation that occurs depends on when and where these cells are found.

Early Embryo Stem Cells

The inner cell mass of the early **embryo** is **pluripotent**, which means the cells that are found there are capable of dividing to form *all types* of specialised cells. All the genes in embryonic stem cells can be switched on.

Organs are made from a combination of tissues which are groups of specialised cells. For example, the heart is made of muscular, nervous, epithelial and connective tissues.

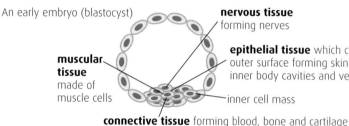

An early embryo (blastocyst)

nervous tissue forming nerves

epithelial tissue which covers the outer surface forming skin and inner body cavities and vessels.

muscular tissue made of muscle cells

inner cell mass

connective tissue forming blood, bone and cartilage

Embryonic Stem Cells

Embryonic cells tend to divide into specialised cells; they do not naturally **self-renew** (replace) themselves. They can, however, be treated in a lab under **in vitro** conditions to form stem cells, which are known as **embryonic stem cells**. This provides a bank of stem cells for research.

Tissue Stem Cells

These are found in specific locations, **replacing** specialised cells that have a limited lifespan or that are damaged, or producing more cells to enable the **growth** of the tissue. Tissue stem cells are multipotent, which means that their ability to differentiate is **limited** to the tissue they come from.

Some tissue stem cells do not become specialised but **self-renew** (divide to make more stem cells) in order to maintain a stock to last the organism's lifetime.

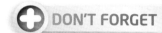

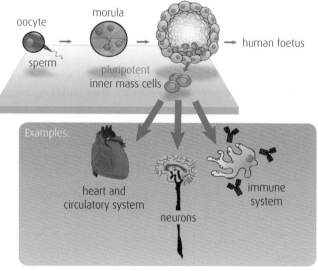

blastocyst

morula

oocyte

sperm

pluripotent inner mass cells

→ human foetus

Examples:

heart and circulatory system

neurons

immune system

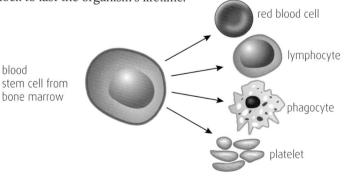

red blood cell

lymphocyte

blood stem cell from bone marrow

phagocyte

platelet

 THINGS TO DO AND THINK ABOUT

1 What types of genes are expressed in a specialised somatic cell?

2 Explain the difference between pluripotent and multipotent stem cells?

3 Why do some tissue stem cells self-renew?

STEM CELLS

STEM CELL RESEARCH

Stem cell research gives a better understanding of the control of gene expression and differentiation. Stem cells are also used to model cells and tissues, to study the effects of diseases or drug therapy. A limitation of this research is that it can't look at interactions within the organism. A key aim is to promote the therapeutic use of stem cells to replace damaged or diseased tissue. Stem cell production is under strict control.

RESEARCH AND THERAPEUTIC USES OF STEM CELLS

Therapeutic value looks at the potential of stem cells in medicine. Stem cells are of special interest in the **repair of diseased or damaged organs and to replace lost tissue**.

Skin Grafts

If a person is badly burned, there may not be enough good skin to use in grafts. A solution is to remove some adult stem cells from an area of good skin. These can then be cultured in the laboratory to produce skin cells. The new skin is grafted onto affected areas on the patient. The skin will not be rejected but isn't perfect as it lacks the complexity of normal skin, not having hair follicles and sweat glands.

Cornea Repair

Damaged corneas are more usually removed and replaced with healthy corneas from dead donors. This procedure is tried and tested, but is invasive and there is a global lack of donors. Scientists have found that multipotent stem cells are located at the edge of the cornea. They can produce corneal or conjunctival cells. Stem cells can be removed from the patient's 'good' eye to be transplanted onto the damaged eye. Studies have included the use of contact lenses as culture media for the stem cells.

ETHICAL ISSUES OF STEM CELL USE

Certain control measures are in place to try to address some of the ethical implications of stem cell use.

Moral

Unused blastocysts from embryonic stem cell lines are destroyed as they are not allowed to develop beyond day 14. This is when the embryo would normally implant in the uterus leading to development of a foetus.

Health

A complete medical history of tissue stem cell donors is required to minimise the chance of recipients developing other medical problems.

Safety

Stem cells must be safe to use in the treatment of patients: they should not cause other conditions or diseases such as tumours. It is for this reason that ongoing research and thorough testing is vital.

CANCER

Healthy cells spend most of their lifecycle growing and performing their specialised roles. A short portion of their lifecycle is spent dividing in mitosis. Checkpoints in the lifecycle ensure that that the cell has grown sufficiently and completed DNA replication before division. A cell undergoes a limited number of cell divisions before it dies. Some genes produce regulatory proteins that promote division and act like an accelerator, others stop or slow division and act like brakes.

Normal cells have a programmed lifespan, controlled by regulatory signals, and are replaced by cell division when they die, so that organs maintain both structure and function. A cancer cell does not respond to regulatory signals. It doesn't undergo this pre-programmed 'death' but divides rapidly to form a space-occupying mass or tumour.

normal tissue

Cancer cells lack these controls because of mutations in the genes that control mitosis. The cells divide rapidly and form a tumour. A cancerous tumour has a blood supply that feeds the cells with nutrients and oxygen for rapid growth. Healthy cells normally stick to each other, but cancer cells lose this ability and separate. The blood vessels that supply them allow cells to escape and spread to other parts of the body to form secondary tumours.

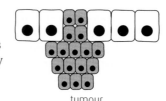

tumour

VIDEO LINK

Watch the animation on cancer formation at www. brightredbooks.net

THINGS TO DO AND THINK ABOUT

1 Where are germline cells located?

2 What is produced when germline cells divide by:
   a mitosis?   **b** meiosis?

3 Describe the mechanisms that cause the formation and spread of cancerous tumours.

4 Use the passage below to develop moral, health and safety arguments for and against the therapeutic use of stem cells. Use your answer to justify the current position whereby ethical committees, rather than individual health care professionals and patients, decide whether the technique can be used.

ONLINE TEST

Test yourself on your knowledge of stem cells at www.brightredbooks.net

Parkinson's disease is a degenerative brain condition. It is characterised by the loss of neural cells that produce a chemical called dopamine. There is currently no cure but researchers are trying to find the best combination of stem cells and hormones to generate these dopamine-producing cells. Embryonic cells have been used with some success, but animal studies have shown that there is a risk of developing tumours. The limited nature of tissue stem cells means that a suitable source has yet to be found. Work is being done with tissue cells that have been chemically treated or induced to form a suitable stem cell, but this has yet to produce the perfect cell bank.

THE STRUCTURE OF DNA

Deoxyribonucleic acid (DNA) contains the code to make all of the tens of thousands of proteins in an organism. Proteins, in the form of enzymes, catalyse reactions to manufacture a complete individual that is correct for its species. A gene is a region of DNA that codes for the specific sequence of amino acids that forms a polypeptide chain. The polypeptide chain can be modified and folded to form a protein.

This genetic code is passed on through generations when gametes fuse during fertilisation. Thus, the genetic code is inherited.

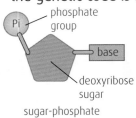

phosphate group

Pi

base

deoxyribose sugar

sugar-phosphate backbone

strong chemical bond

A

G

T

C

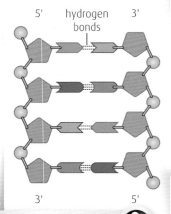

5'   hydrogen bonds   3'

3'   5'

THE STRUCTURE OF DNA

DNA is made up of sub-units called nucleotides, joined in strands. There are four types of nucleotide, depending on the base: adenine (A), thymine (T), cytosine (C) and guanine (G). Each strand is made up of nucleotides which form strong chemical bonds between a phosphate group of one nucleotide and the deoxyribose of another nucleotide: the sugar–phosphate backbone. The DNA molecule is double-stranded due to the formation of weak hydrogen bonds between the bases: adenine always bonds with thymine (A–T) and cytosine always bonds with guanine (C–G). The base sequence of DNA forms the genetic code.

The strands are anti-parallel, meaning that they run in opposite directions. Each strand has a 3' end and a 5' end, determined by whether the third or fifth carbon on the sugar molecule of the nucleotide is closest to the end. The double-stranded DNA molecule twists to form a double helix.

5'   0
4'   1'
3'   2'

CHROMOSOMES

The DNA is located in the membrane-bound nucleus and takes the form of chromosomes. The DNA in each chromosome is extremely long and thread-like; it must, therefore, be organised into tidy spools (a bit like spools of thread), so it cannot get tangled up. Each spool is composed of proteins with the DNA tightly coiled around them. This is how 2 metres of DNA is packed into the microscopic nucleus of every cell in the human body!

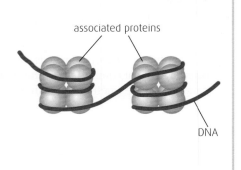

associated proteins

DNA

DNA REPLICATION

DNA must be replicated (duplicated) before cell division can occur, ensuring daughter (new) cells have a complete set of genetic information. Mitosis is the type of division that replaces diploid body cells; meiosis is the type that produces haploid gametes.

STAGES OF DNA REPLICATION

Requirements for replication:

- DNA
- ATP
- DNA polymerase (enzyme)

- the four types of nucleotide
- primer (a short sequence of nucleotides)
- ligase (enzyme).

contd

VIDEO LINK

The video clip at www. brightredbooks.net gives a nice animation of our tightly coiled and packed DNA.

DON'T FORGET

Nuclear DNA is tightly coiled with associated proteins to form linear thread-like chromosomes.

1 The DNA molecule **unwinds**.
2 Hydrogen bonds break, '**unzipping**' the molecule and exposing the bases of both DNA strands.
3 A **primer** attaches to the **3'** end of each exposed DNA template strand.
4 This initiates **DNA polymerase** to add free complementary DNA nucleotides to the **3'** end of the growing strand.
5 **Hydrogen bonds** form between the bases.
6 Strong **chemical bonds** form between the phosphate and deoxyribose sugar of adjacent nucleotides.
7 **Ligase** enzyme joins the fragments to form a complete strand.
8 Each replicated DNA molecule is made of one original template strand and a newly synthesised strand.

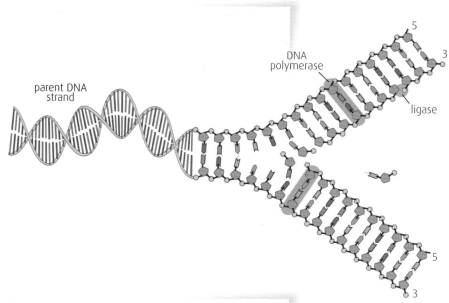

parent DNA strand

DNA polymerase

ligase

DIRECTION OF REPLICATION

DNA polymerase adds nucleotides on to the 3' end of the strand. The strands run in opposite directions, which means that one strand can be built up continuously as the molecule exposes the 3'-end nucleotide – this is the **leading strand**.

However, the other strand faces the wrong way to add nucleotides to the 3' end. Synthesis using this strand lags behind until enough of the template strand is exposed to add a primer and then add nucleotides to the 3' end. This is repeated as more template becomes exposed, producing fragments. A complete strand is made when the fragments are joined together by the enzyme **ligase**. This strand is the **lagging strand**.

unzipping continues as replication takes place

5'–old strand
A C G T G G A C
| | | | | | | |
T G C A C C T G
3'–old strand

unzipping region

G T T G A C G — 3'–old strand
   A A C T G C — the leading strand
            5'–new strand

T G A A C G T C — 3'–new strand
A C T T G C A G — the lagging strand
            5'–old strand

VIDEO LINK

Find out more about mitochondrial DNA at www.brightredbooks.net

 THINGS TO DO AND THINK ABOUT

1 A molecule of DNA was found to be composed of 32% adenine. Express the ratio of thymine to guanine as a simple whole-number ratio.

2 Label the following on the diagram of a section of DNA:

  a The molecules represented by numbers 1–4.

  b Show the 3' and 5' ends by adding labels to the blank boxes.

  c Name the type of bonds labelled A and B.

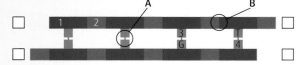

DON'T FORGET

Each strand can only be replicated in the 5' to 3' direction.

3 Complete this diagram to show the direction of DNA replication. Show the 3' and 5' ends and draw the leading strand with a continuous line and the lagging strand with a broken line.

ONLINE TEST

Take the test on DNA online at www.brightredbooks.net

POLYMERASE CHAIN REACTION (PCR)

DNA replication occurs naturally in cells before cell division. Given the correct conditions, DNA fragments can be amplified, through repeated cycles of artificial replication in laboratories, by a process known as the polymerase chain reaction.

STAGES OF PCR

Requirements:

- an original DNA sample to provide the template
- a stock of the four types of DNA nucleotides
- heat-tolerant DNA polymerase (an enzyme)
- a thermal cycler (an automated reaction vessel)
- buffer solution (maintains an optimum pH)
- copies of complementary DNA primers for the start of each strand of the target fragment (which target the fragment to be amplified).

Heat-tolerant (thermostable) polymerase is obtained from bacteria that live around hot springs and which are able to withstand high temperatures without their proteins being denatured.

DON'T FORGET

A primer is needed to start the synthesis of a DNA strand. Primers are short nucleotide sequences that are complementary to the start of the DNA sequence to be copied. They are needed because DNA polymerase can only build a strand by adding nucleotides to the end of an existing sequence.

PCR PROCESS

1   DNA is heated to about 95°C to separate the original DNA strands.

2   The sample is cooled to about 55°C. Complementary primers are added and these bind (anneal) to the start of each strand.

3   The sample is heated to about 72°C and heat-tolerant DNA polymerase is added.

4   Complementary free DNA nucleotides are added to the 3' end of the new strands.

5   The number of original molecules has now doubled – this is called amplification.

Steps 1–5 are repeated, amplifying the DNA to make many copies.

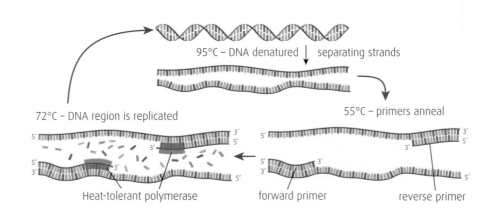

95°C – DNA denatured | separating strands

72°C – DNA region is replicated

55°C – primers anneal

Heat-tolerant polymerase

forward primer

reverse primer

PRACTICAL APPLICATIONS OF PCR

1 DNA Profiling

If only a tiny quantity of genetic material is found at a crime scene, PCR can provide enough material for various tests, such as genetic fingerprinting. Each individual has unique repeats of sequences. Specific probes are incubated with the crime-scene sample and with a sample from a suspect. If comparison of the two samples provides a match, there is a high degree of certainty that the suspect has been identified. This same method can be used to identify unknown victims or dead persons by comparing their DNA with close relatives.

2 Research

PCR can be used to build up a large bank of material from a small initial source, such as a mutated gene sequence. The stock can then be subjected to several types of analyses and can even be divided up so that several research teams can work on it.

3 Early Detection of Infection

PCR can be used to amplify viral DNA when only a few cells out of millions are infected, such as in the case of early HIV infection.

4 Diagnostics

Amplified stocks of DNA can be tested for a known genetic condition. If a mutation is found, the individual can be given advice on their chances of developing the disease.

Other diagnostic methods include:

1 **Archaeobiology**: the DNA found in mummified bodies, skeletal remains or insects trapped in amber is usually highly degraded. However, small intact samples may be amplified and sequenced to look for connections to other mummified remains, find living relations or build a picture of life at that time.

2 **Phylogenetics**: this maps when species split from each other in evolution by how much their DNA differs. Again, small samples from mummified or fossil evidence can be used.

5 DNA Paternity Testing

DNA from a woman's offspring and adult males are amplified by PCR. The samples are then cut with enzymes and the resulting fragments compared. A child will receive 50% of their alleles from their biological father.

The oral contraceptive pill prevents the release of FSH and LH from the pituitary gland.

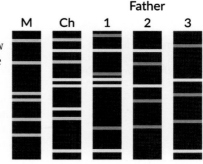

VIDEO LINK

Learn more about PCR by watching the clip at www. brightredbooks.net

DON'T FORGET

PCR gives researchers large stocks of target DNA that can be tested in a variety of ways or stored for future research.

THINGS TO DO AND THINK ABOUT

1 Explain why it is necessary to increase the temperature to around 95°C during a PCR cycle, then cool it to about 55°C.

2 Heat-tolerant DNA polymerase is obtained from bacteria that live in the margins of hot springs and are adapted to withstand a temperature range of 50 to 80°C. What would happen if you used DNA polymerase from bacteria that live in a temperature range from –5 to 45°C?

3 Look at the PCR temperature graph below.

    A How many cycles are shown on the graph?

    B At what time was the second cycle annealing complete?

    C There were three DNA fragments at the start. How many were present after 34 minutes?

    D What was added at 8 minutes?

    E Predict the time when five cycles would be complete.

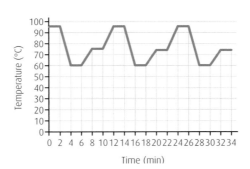

ONLINE TEST

Test your knowledge of PCR at www.brightredbooks.net

GENE EXPRESSION

Gene expression involves the processes of transcription and translation of DNA sequences into proteins. The original DNA template contains the code to make protein. However, it also contains non-coding sections.

The coding regions are called **exons** and the non-coding regions are called **introns**. The functions of different non-coding regions of DNA are:

- to regulate transcription – there are binding sites for other chemicals that can switch off neighbouring genes
- to be transcribed to form RNAs that are not translated into protein, for example tRNA, rRNA and RNA fragments
- unknown – some regions make no sense and are thought to be the result of mistakes.

DON'T FORGET

There are three different types of RNA: mRNA, tRNA and rRNA. Sections of DNA code for RNA.

GENE EXPRESSION 1: TRANSCRIPTION

Gene expression involves the transcription (copying) and translation of the DNA sequence into protein.

The primary structure of a protein is determined by the sequence of nucleotide bases in a DNA strand which cannot leave the nucleus.

The code must therefore be copied, carried outside the nucleus and translated into protein on the ribosome. This is possible because of three different types of RNA.

RNA

Ribonucleic acid (RNA) is a single-stranded molecule made of nucleotide sub-units. Each nucleotide consists of a phosphate group, ribose sugar and a base. There are four different bases: adenine, uracil, guanine and cytosine. Uracil is complementary to adenine.

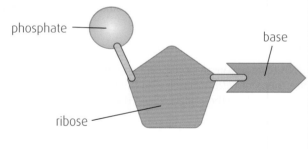

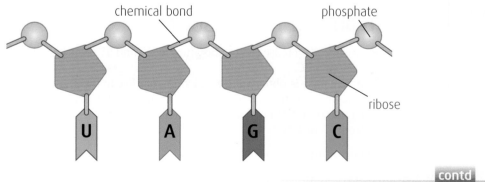

contd

You should be familiar with the following types of RNA, all of which are involved in protein synthesis.

1 **Messenger RNA (mRNA)** is formed during transcription of DNA in the nucleus and is the template for protein synthesis at the ribosomes. It dictates the sequence of amino acids in the protein being synthesised.

2 **Transfer RNA (tRNA)** carries specific amino acids to the ribosomes for translation of the genetic code. Base pairing within tRNA molecules causes the tRNA to fold into a clover-leaf shape with two distinct regions: an exposed triplet anticodon site and an attachment site for a specific amino acid. The anticodon matches to its complementary triplet codon on the mRNA strand, bringing its specific amino acid with it.

3 **Ribosomal RNA (rRNA)** binds to proteins to form ribosomes. A ribosome is composed of two sub-units, one large and one small and is the site of protein synthesis; the small sub-unit 'reads' the code on mRNA and the large sub-unit provides active sites so that two tRNAs can bring their amino acids next to each other allowing peptide bonds to form between them.

RNA is transcribed from DNA. mRNA is translated into protein but tRNA and rRNA are not translated into protein.

ONLINE

Find out more about RNA at www.brightredbooks.net

	DNA	mRNA
Type of sugar	Deoxyribose	Ribose
Bases	Adenine, cytosine, guanine and **thymine**	Adenine, cytosine, guanine and **uracil**
Number of strands	Two	One
Location	Only in nucleus	Moves from nucleus to cytoplasm

Comparison of DNA and mRNA

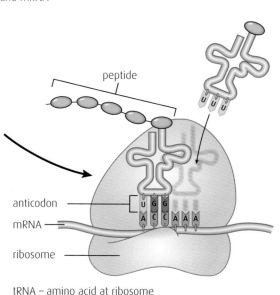

tRNA – amino acid at ribosome

ONLINE TEST

Revise your knowledge of this topic by taking the test at www.brightredbooks.net

THINGS TO DO AND THINK ABOUT

1 Compare the structures of DNA and mRNA.

2 Summarise the roles of the three types of RNA.

3 Draw and label a molecule of tRNA.

4 Where in the cell could you find:

  a mRNA   **b** tRNA   **c** rRNA.

PROTEIN SYNTHESIS

TRANSCRIPTION

The first stage of protein synthesis takes place in the nucleus and is called transcription. An mRNA molecule is produced that carries the genetic code from the DNA in the nucleus to a ribosome in the cytoplasm. Production of mRNA is essential, as DNA is too large to pass through the nuclear membrane.

Transcription produces a primary mRNA transcript using RNA polymerase which:

1   moves along the DNA double helix unwinding it as it goes.

2   breaks the hydrogen bonds between complementary bases

3   adds free RNA nucleotides to their complementary bases on the DNA template strand.

Then:

4   the adjacent RNA nucleotides form a strand by forming sugar–phosphate bonds,

5   hydrogen bonds holding the mRNA strand to DNA template break

6   the mRNA moves out of the nucleus.

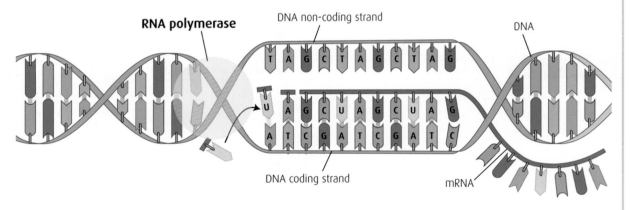

RNA polymerase   DNA non-coding strand   DNA

DNA coding strand   mRNA

DON'T FORGET

The functions of non-coding regions are not mandatory knowledge in your CfE Higher Human Biology course but it is useful to understand why they are present.

RNA SPLICING

The original DNA template contains the code to make protein. However, it also contains non-coding sections. The primary mRNA transcript is modified by removing non-coding sections to form a mature mRNA transcript.

exon	intron	exon	intron	exon	intron	exon	intron

After the primary transcript has been produced, the introns must be cut out.

exon		exon		exon		exon

	intron		intron		intron		intron

The exons join together to produce a **mature mRNA** strand. The order of the exons is unchanged by this process.

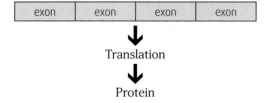

exon	exon	exon	exon

↓

Translation

↓

Protein

GENE EXPRESSION 2: TRANSLATION

The mRNA molecule that is formed during transcription leaves the nucleus via a nuclear pore and attaches to a **ribosome**. The ribosome is made up of two units composed of ribosomal RNA (rRNA) and proteins. The genetic code is now ready to be translated into an amino acid sequence.

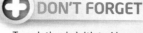
DON'T FORGET

Translation is initiated by a start codon and ends with a stop codon.

1 Translation is initiated by the start codon (AUG) on the mRNA strand. The codon refers to triplets of bases on the mRNA strand.

2 Transfer RNA (tRNA) molecules become attached to amino acid molecules in the cytoplasm. Each type of amino acid attaches to a specific tRNA molecule. The anticodon is a triplet of bases on tRNA. It is complementary to the mRNA codon and carries a specific amino acid to its correct location in a newly forming polypeptide chain.

3 tRNA molecules in the cytoplasm transport amino acids to the ribosome.

4 The first tRNA molecule moves in by means of base pairing between the anticodon on the tRNA molecule and the complementary codon on the mRNA strand.

5 Another tRNA molecule carries an amino acid to the ribosome. Complementary pairing between codon and anticodon brings the amino acids in line beside each other. A peptide bond forms between the amino acids.

6 The first tRNA molecule detaches from the mRNA and is free to collect another amino acid from the cytoplasm.

7 As translation progresses, the ribosome moves along the mRNA molecule exposing the third codon, allowing a third tRNA molecule to bring a third amino acid into position.

8 This process repeats until the stop codon (UGA) is reached at the 3' end of the mRNA strand and the newly formed polypeptide chain is complete.

transcription

nucleus

mRNA nucleotides

mRNA

translation

mRNA

ribosome

cytoplasm

polypeptide chain

VIDEO LINK

Watch the clip at www. brightredbooks.net for an overview of protein synthesis that includes the roles of different RNA molecules.

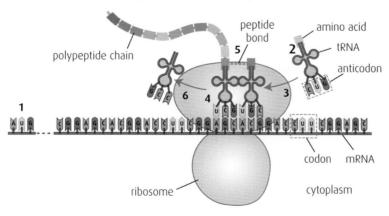

peptide bond

amino acid

tRNA

anticodon

polypeptide chain

codon   mRNA

ribosome

cytoplasm

THINGS TO DO AND THINK ABOUT

1 Write the complementary mRNA code to this strand of DNA:

   AGGCTAACTGCAATCGAAATG

2 List all the raw materials required for transcription to take place.

3 Describe the sequence of events leading to transcription.

4 What is the difference between an intron and an exon?

5 How does a primary transcript differ from a mature mRNA strand?

ONLINE TEST

Head to www. brightredbooks.net and test yourself on this topic.

ONE GENE, MANY PROTEINS

AFTER TRANSCRIPTION

One **gene** may code for more than one protein. The codes for different proteins may be made by cutting out alternative regions (splicing) of the primary **mRNA transcript**. An **intron** (non-coding region) for one protein may be an **exon** (coding region) for a different protein. When the mature mRNA transcript is forming all the introns are removed BUT some of the exons may be removed too. Different mature mRNA transcripts are formed depending on which exons are kept. This means that different proteins can be formed during translation.

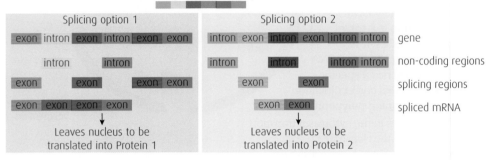

VIDEO LINK

Find out about some of the things that proteins do at www.brightredbooks.net

STRUCTURE OF PROTEINS

Amino acids are held together by peptide bonds to form polypeptides.

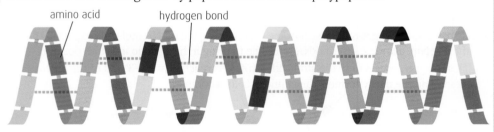

The polypeptide chain folds to form a three-dimensional shape. The three-dimensional shape is determined by **hydrogen bonds** that hold the chains together and other interactions between amino acids, which cause it to twist and fold in specific ways; hydrophobic areas of the chain move inwards and away from the watery external environment, and positively and negatively charged amino acids move towards each other.

The shape of the protein determines its function. The properties of the proteins produced determines the **phenotype** of the individual.

contd

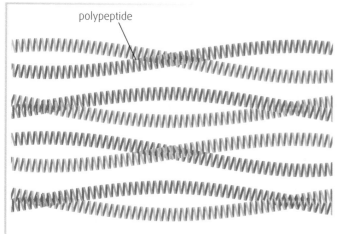

polypeptide

fibrous proteins – flat sheets

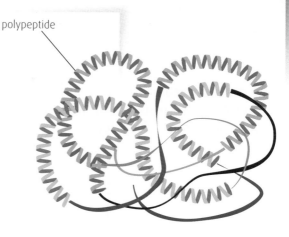

polypeptide

globular proteins – wound into a ball

PHENOTYPE

Gene expression determines the phenotype of an organism. The proteins produced (enzymes, hormones, structural and transport proteins) all work together to determine the characteristics that are typical for a species. A specialised cell, such as a skeletal muscle cell, expresses two types of gene: those that are vital for its maintenance, such as the genes coding for respiratory enzymes, and those that are vital for its specialised function, for example the genes coding for the slow- and fast-twitch muscle fibres. All other genes are switched off. Characteristics that are unique to the individual (such as height and body mass) are the result of genotype and are influenced by intracellular and extracellular environmental factors. Diet, activity levels, stress levels and infection can all affect an organism's internal environment, triggering changes in pH, chemical and hormone production. This, in turn, affects gene expression by switching genes on or off.

DON'T FORGET

All proteins on Earth are made from a combination of 20 amino acids which are held together by peptide bonds. Different combinations and numbers of amino acids result in different proteins.

THINGS TO DO AND THINK ABOUT

1   What type of bond is responsible for:
    a   connecting amino acids together in the polypeptide
    b   coiling of the polypeptide chain
    c   forming the three-dimensional shape of the protein?

2   How does post-transcriptional modification result in different proteins?

ONLINE TEST

How well have you learned this topic? Test yourself online at www.brightredbooks.net

MUTATIONS

A **mutation** can cause a change in the amino acid sequence, or in the number of amino acids in a protein. The resultant protein may be either **absent** (because it no longer functions) or **faulty**, causing **genetic disorders**.

SINGLE-BASE MUTATIONS

Individual genes are affected by **point mutations**. If the sequence of DNA bases in a gene is altered, the corresponding sequence of amino acids may change, possibly altering the protein produced. Think about the mutations in the diagram.

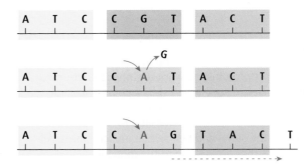

Normal strand of DNA

Substitution – one of the bases is replaced by a different base (here A replaces G). This can result in **nonsense**, **missense** and **splice-site** mutations.

Insertion – an extra base is inserted into the sequence, in this example A, moving the bases after the insertion one place to the right. This is a **frame-shift mutation**, as every amino acid after the point of insertion is altered.

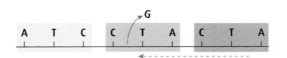

Deletion – a base is removed from the sequence, in this example G, shifting the bases one place to the left. This is another **frame-shift mutation**, as every amino acid after the point of deletion is altered.

CONSEQUENCES OF POINT MUTATIONS

DNA triplets code for specific amino acids. There are 20 amino acids but 64 triplets (from the possible combinations of the four nucleotide bases A, T, C and G arranged in sets of three). So, an amino acid may be coded by several triplets. This means that a mutation can have any one of four consequences:

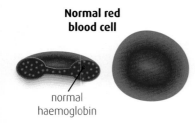

Normal red blood cell

normal haemoglobin

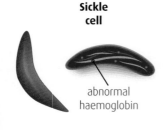

Sickle cell

abnormal haemoglobin

1   **Missense**: the substituted nucleotide results in a triplet that codes for a different amino acid, which may change the function of the protein. This is seen in sickle-cell disease – red blood cells are malformed (sickle-shaped), reducing their oxygen-carrying capacity. In some cases, it may have little effect on the protein.

2   **Nonsense**: the substituted nucleotide results in a stop codon, so the polypeptide chain is shorter. This occurs in Duchenne muscular dystrophy, which causes a progressive weakening of muscles and reduced life expectancy, mainly in males.

3   **Splice-site mutations**: a substitution mutation at a splice site may mean that some introns are not cut out but remain in the mRNA sequence. These introns will be read during translation and the protein will have extra amino acids which will alter the sequence and, therefore, function of the protein. Similarly, some exons might not be included in the mature transcript, missing out important amino acids and therefore altering the protein.

4   **Frame-shift**: this is the result of a deletion or insertion mutation and the entire sequence of triplets after this point will be wrong. This has a major effect on the structure of the protein produced. An example of a condition caused by this type of mutation is Tay-Sachs syndrome; a progressive disease of the nervous system which becomes obvious at 6 months of age. Affected children have a life expectancy of 3 to 5 years.

CHROMOSOME STRUCTURE MUTATIONS

Whole sections of chromosomes can be altered by mutation, affecting several genes. Such changes are often lethal.

Duplication

Genes from one of a pair of homologous chromosomes transfer to the other, leading to duplication of genes.

Myoglobin and haemoglobin are thought to have evolved from a common ancestral gene that duplicated and, subsequently, mutated.

Gene 1 Gene 2 Gene 3 Gene 4   Gene 7 Gene 8

Gene 5 Gene 6

Gene 1 Gene 2 Gene 3 Gene 4 Gene 5 Gene 6 Gene 5 Gene 6 Gene 7 Gene 8

Deletion

Genes are lost from a chromosome.

Gene 1 Gene 2 Gene 3 Gene 4 Gene 5 Gene 6 Gene 7 Gene 8

Gene 3 Gene 4

Gene 1 Gene 2 Gene 5 Gene 6 Gene 7 Gene 8

Inversion

A section of the chromosome is reversed

Gene 1 Gene 2 Gene 3 Gene 4 Gene 5 Gene 6 Gene 7 Gene 8

Gene 1 Gene 2 Gene 3 Gene 4 Gene 5 Gene 6 Gene 7 Gene 8

Gene 1 Gene 2 Gene 3 Gene 5 Gene 4 Gene 6 Gene 7 Gene 8

Translocation

Sections are swapped between different chromosomes (not homologous partners).

Gene 1 Gene 2 Gene 3 Gene 4 Gene 5 ┊ Gene 6 Gene 7 Gene 8

Gene A Gene B Gene C Gene D Gene E Gene F

Gene A Gene B Gene C Gene D Gene E Gene F Gene 6 Gene 7 Gene 8

VIDEO LINK

Learn more about mutation by watching the clips at www.brightredbooks.net

DON'T FORGET

Mutations affect proteins: by altering the amino acid sequence and thereby the protein function; by causing the loss of a protein; by duplicating or altering regulatory instructions, giving excess protein, or by creating different combinations of proteins.

THINGS TO DO AND THINK ABOUT

1   Redraw these chromosomes to illustrate the following chromosome structure mutations:
    a   translocation
    b   duplication
    c   deletion.

2   A section of DNA has the following sequence: ATGCAGTAC. What type of gene mutation is represented by each of the following altered sequences?
    a   ACGCAGTAC
    b   ATGCATAC
    c   ATGCATGTAC

ONLINE TEST

How well have you learned about mutations? Test yourself at www.brightredbooks.net

HUMAN GENOMICS

All of the genes in an organism (along with the other DNA sequences that do not code for proteins) are known collectively as the **genome**, and the study of the genome is known as **genomics**. Technology has enabled scientists to determine the nucleotide sequence of specific genes and the entire genomes of certain species.

A comparison of sequence data has revealed that different species are surprisingly similar, which suggests that the genome is **highly conserved**.

ONLINE

Explore the human genome by following the NCBI link at www.brightredbooks.net

ONLINE

Use the link at www.brightredbooks.net to study the protein linked to retinitis pigmentosa, a condition affecting vision. You will follow the protein's story from gene sequence to structure.

DON'T FORGET

Bioinformatics is the use of automated computer analyses to determine the sequence of DNA. The infomation has to be stored in vast databases.

SEQUENCING DNA

DNA can be sequenced using automated computer analyses – a branch of science known as **bioinformatics**.

Each chromosome contains many million nucleotide base pairs but sequencers can only determine a few hundred at a time. The solution is to make copies of the DNA to be sequenced.

Base sequences are identified using computer programs. They can quickly compare sequences of different species. **Computer and statistical analysis** is then used to track divergence from the common ancestor and to examine how closely related the species are.

DNA sequencing generates massive amounts of data; the smallest chromosome in the human complement contains over 51 million nucleotide base pairs and there are about three billion nucleotides in the human genome. The data is stored in specialist **databases** around the world, such as the National Center for Biotechnology Information, NCBI, or the Human Genome Mutation Database, HGMD. The databases are available via the **internet** and are accessed by scientists for further **analyses** and **comparison**.

USES OF BIOINFORMATICS

Finding Gene Sequences

This can be achieved by:

- matching a sequence to a similar sequence in a database
- finding a **start** codon and sequencing until the **stop** codon is identified
- working backwards to identify all the possible DNA sequences from the amino acid sequence in a protein.

Species of importance to humans have been targeted for DNA sequencing: crop plants, farm animals, crop pests and organisms that cause disease in humans or food species. The information may be used, for example, to develop genetically enhanced crops or to find alternatives to the chemical control of agricultural pests and pathogens.

PERSONAL GENOMICS

The human genome sequence was completed in 2003 and provides a reference database. Individuals all have slight variations in their sequences, which can provide information about their risk of developing certain diseases or conditions, the potential effectiveness of certain medicines or the risk of developing serious side effects of treatment. Assessing risk is a complex task as mutations are not always harmful.

contd

Pharmacogenetics and Personalised Medicine

An individual's personal genome sequence could, therefore, be used to predict the risk of developing conditions, allowing them to make lifestyle choices to reduce the risks; it could also be used to inform the prescription of the most effective drugs. This type of personalised medicine is known as **pharmacogenetics**. An individual's genome could provide information that would enable the selection of the most effective drugs at dosages that would better balance effectiveness with harmful side effects.

It is important to note that the development of a disease is often due to a combination of genetics and modifiable factors, such as diet, activity and stress levels. Genetic information could, therefore, be misinterpreted if taken out of context. There are also ethical implications regarding the right of access to genetic information by prospective employers and insurers.

GENE PROBES

Gene probes are used to find target sequences in DNA.

Gene probes are short, synthetic, single strands of DNA which are complementary to the sequence of interest. These probes need to be identifiable, so have other compounds attached, such as fluorescent labels.

Fluorescent Labelling

Fluorescent probes can be incubated with whole cells or chromosomes, and these viewed with a fluorescence microscope. Often the fluorescence is weak; the solution is to amplify DNA fragments using PCR to give a larger sample and, therefore, a stronger fluorescence. The fragments are separated by electrophoresis: samples are loaded into wells in a gel and an electric current applied, which separates the fragments according to size and charge. Any fragments that contain the target sequence will be fluorescent and can be seen under a UV light.

THINGS TO DO AND THINK ABOUT

Use the link at www.brightredbooks.net to identify the amino acid sequence of this section of DNA code:

ACGTGCTGCCGACGAGGCATCCGAAACCTTCTTTAG

How many amino acids does the sequence encode?

What does the final triplet stand for?

Press the **RELATE FUNCTION** button to find out which proteins contain this sequence.

ONLINE TEST

Take the test on genomic factors at www.brightredbooks.net

METABOLISM

METABOLIC PATHWAYS

Within the cell, reactions can be classed as:

- **anabolic** reactions – large molecules are synthesised from several smaller ones, with energy being used up
- **catabolic** reactions – large molecules are broken down into smaller molecules, usually with a release of energy.

The sum of all the anabolic and catabolic reactions that occur within a living cell is collectively known as the cell's **metabolism**.

A metabolic pathway is a series of chemical reactions that follow on, one after another. Each stage in the pathway is controlled by an enzyme, with the product of one reaction becoming the substrate for the next. The rate of reaction of key enzymes is carefully regulated. The reactions are often **reversible**.

In the example shown below, compound X will be converted into compound Y, as long as the concentration of X remains relatively high compared to that of compound Y. If the concentration of X decreases, the reaction will proceed in the opposite direction.

In this way, enzymes act to drive reactions towards equilibrium, where the relative concentrations of molecules at the start and end of the reaction are balanced.

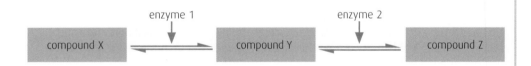

Some reactions are **irreversible**, which means the reaction will not go in the opposite direction. This is usually because the reaction has gone to completion and the products are stable, meaning they will no longer react with each other.

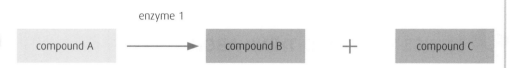

DON'T FORGET

Building molecules uses energy and breaking molecules releases energy.

Chemicals can take part in more than one reaction. This means that they can take **alternative routes**, as in the diagram below.

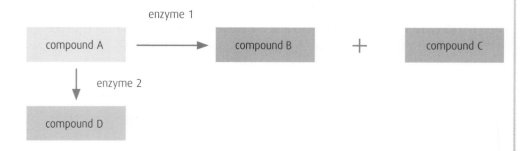

SWITCHING GENES ON AND OFF

As all cells inherit a complete set of genetic information during mitosis, each cell has the potential to produce protein from every gene in the code. However, different types of cells only make the proteins required by that cell type for normal function. This means that there must be a mechanism which allows genes to be 'switched on' and 'switched off'.

Regulating Gene Expression

The triggers to regulate gene expression may come from outside the cell in response to changes in the internal environment. The body has numerous receptors that can detect changes in the body, e.g. blood water concentration. This may cause different concentrations of hormones to be secreted which will bind to receptors on specific target cells and initiate a cascade of reactions that trigger the expression of certain genes and bring levels to a normal state.

Some regions of DNA regulate gene expression. They code for small molecules that can inhibit or trigger the transcription of genes, and others may affect the translation of proteins. Such refined control of gene expression ensures that the unnecessary production of large proteins is avoided. This saves the use of the cell's precious resources: for example the gene coding for an enzyme might be inhibited in this way in the absence of its substrate, as it would make no sense to produce an enzyme with no work to do.

VIDEO LINK

Explore this topic further by watching the clip at www. brightredbooks.net

THINGS TO DO AND THINK ABOUT

1 Explain why lactate, produced by fermentation, can be returned to the aerobic respiration pathway in the presence of oxygen but ethanol and CO_2 cannot.

2 Why is the expression of some genes sometimes 'switched off'?

3 Explain why a liver cell looks and functions differently from a skeletal muscle cell.

ONLINE TEST

Test your knowledge of this topic online at www. brightredbooks.net

ENZYME ACTION

ACTIVATION ENERGY

At normal body temperature and without enzymes, chemical reactions would take place at too slow a rate to maintain life. Chemical reactions involve breaking chemical bonds and forming new ones. To start a reaction, energy (the activation energy) must be used to break bonds within the reactant molecules. As energy is absorbed, bonds become increasingly unstable. At their most unstable, the molecules are said to be in a **transition state**. When the bonds in the reactants break, the molecular structure of the product forms. Enzymes act by reducing the activation energy required to reach the transition state and, therefore, they allow reactions to take place at a lower temperature.

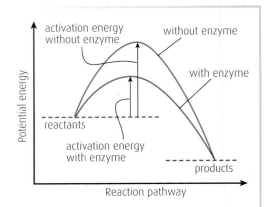

INDUCED FIT

Each enzyme can only act on one substrate. Enzyme action is, therefore, said to be **specific**. This is because the shape of the substrate molecule fits into the enzyme's active site. When two or more substrate molecules are involved in the reaction, the molecules fit into the active site in the particular orientation required to allow the molecules to react.

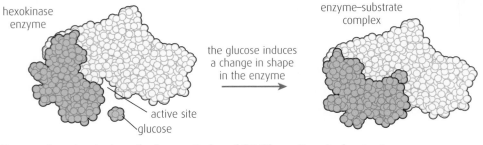

Enzyme function is described as an 'induced fit'. The active site begins in an open position, which allows the substrate (with a high affinity for the active site) to move in and bind. Binding of the substrate causes a change in the shape of the active site to a closed position. This brings the substrate and enzyme closer together, increasing the chance of a reaction. Once the product has formed, the shape of the active site returns to the open position and the product (which has a low affinity for the active site) moves out.

DON'T FORGET

To increase the rate of reaction further, the enzyme concentration would have to be increased.

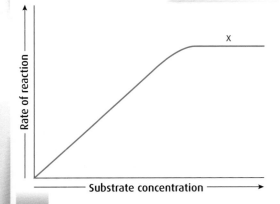

SUBSTRATE CONCENTRATION

As the substrate concentration increases, the rate of reaction increases and then becomes constant. The graph demonstrates how the rate of reaction is linked to the number of active sites that are filled at any one time.

FEEDBACK INHIBITION (END-PRODUCT INHIBITION)

The rate at which some metabolic pathways progress can be controlled by a build-up of the end product. In feedback inhibition, when the end product reaches a critical concentration, the end product binds to one enzyme in the metabolic pathway, altering the shape of this enzyme's active site and stopping the pathway. This prevents too much end product from being produced. As the concentration of the end product drops, inhibition ceases and the pathway resumes again.

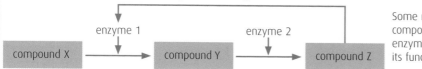
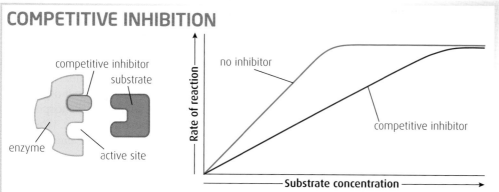

Some molecules of compound Z bind to enzyme 1, inhibiting its function.

COMPETITIVE INHIBITION

Competitive inhibitor molecules have a shape similar to that of the substrate. They bind with the enzyme's active site, preventing the substrate from entering. Because the substrate and inhibitor are in competition for the active site, increasing the substrate concentration causes an increase in the rate of reaction.

NON-COMPETITIVE INHIBITION

Non-competitive inhibitors bind to a part of the enzyme which is not the active site. As a result, the shape of the active site is altered and the substrate cannot enter. Because the substrate and inhibitor are not in competition for the active site, increasing substrate concentration has no effect on the rate of reaction. The rate of reaction remains low.

DON'T FORGET

Cyanide is a non-competitive inhibitor that inhibits aerobic respiration.

VIDEO LINK

Check out the clip at www.brightredbooks.net for more on enzymes.

THINGS TO DO AND THINK ABOUT

1   Describe the induced fit theory of enzyme action.

2   Describe the mechanisms of competitive and non-competitive inhibition.

3   Explain why increasing substrate concentration cannot overcome the effect of non-competitive inhibition.

ONLINE TEST

Take the test on enzymes at www.brightredbooks.net

CELLULAR RESPIRATION

RESPIRATORY SUBSTRATES AND USES OF ENERGY

Molecules which can be broken down to release energy in respiration are called respiratory substrates. The energy that is released is used to fuel cellular processes, such as protein synthesis, contraction of muscle, active transport and DNA replication.

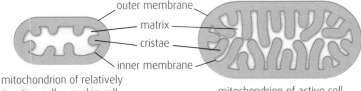

mitochondrion of relatively inactive cell, e.g. skin cell

mitochondrion of active cell, e.g. muscle cell

ATP AND ADP

The series of reactions that make up respiration result in chemical energy being transferred to a molecule called ATP, adenosine triphosphate. ATP is a source of energy that can be used immediately by cells. During respiration, ATP is made when a bond forms between an inorganic phosphate (Pi) and ADP, adenosine diphosphate. This reaction is called **phosphorylation**. When the bond is subsequently broken, the energy is released and used in cellular processes, such as synthetic pathways.

Mitochondria

Mitochondria are known as the power houses of the cell because they are the main site of ATP synthesis.

STAGE ONE – GLYCOLYSIS

Glycolysis is the breakdown of glucose to pyruvate and it takes place in the cytoplasm of every living cell. No oxygen is required. It is divided into an **energy investment phase** and an **energy pay-off phase**.

Initially, the conversion of $2ATP \rightarrow 2ADP + 2Pi$ provides energy for the conversion of glucose to an intermediate phosphorylated molecule (phosphate groups are added to the glucose molecule). The first phosphorylated molecule can take part in alternative reactions.

This phase is followed by the energy pay-off phase in which the intermediate molecules are converted into two pyruvate molecules. As four ATP molecules are produced during this phase, there is a **net gain of two ATP** (4ATP produced, 2ATP used) in glycolysis. Hydrogen ions are released during the energy pay-off phase and are picked up by the hydrogen carrier molecule NAD to make NADH.

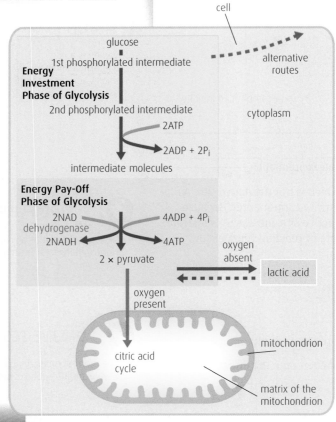

LACTATE METABOLISM

In the absence of oxygen, lactate metabolism takes place. Lactate metabolism produces only the two ATP molecules released in glycolysis. Pyruvate is converted to lactic acid.

DEHYDROGENASE

Dehydrogenase enzyme acts in both glycolysis and the citric acid cycle. It removes **hydrogen** and **electrons** from respiratory intermediates and passes them to the hydrogen carriers NAD to form NADH.

STAGE TWO – CITRIC ACID CYCLE

The citric acid cycle takes place in the matrix of mitochondria in aerobic conditions. Breakdown of pyruvate produces carbon dioxide and an acetyl group. The acetyl group binds with co-enzyme A to produce acetyl co-enzyme A. The acetyl group and oxaloacetate then combine to produce citrate. During a series of enzyme-controlled reactions, citrate is gradually converted back to oxaloacitate. As the cycle proceeds, carbon dioxide is released and hydrogen ions are picked up by NAD to form NADH. NADH carries the hydrogen ions to the third stage of respiration, the electron transport chain, on the inner membrane of the mitochondrion.

ELECTRON TRANSPORT CHAIN

The electron transport chain is found on the inner membrane of the mitochondria and consists of a series of carrier proteins. Hydrogen ions and electrons are transferred from **NADH** to the electron transport chain. As the electrons are passed down the chain, energy is released. Energy that is released from the electron transport chain is used to pump hydrogen ions (hydrogen ions) from the matrix to the intermembrane space, causing a hydrogen ion concentration gradient to develop. Hydrogen ions return to the matrix by flowing through a channel in the enzyme ATP synthase. This flow of ions causes parts of the enzyme molecule to rotate in a clockwise direction, changing the shape of the active site and allowing the conversion of ADP + Pi to ATP.

Electrons are finally passed to oxygen, which binds with hydrogen ions in the matrix to produce water.

ONLINE TEST

How well have you learned about cellular respiration? Take the test online at www.brightredbooks.net

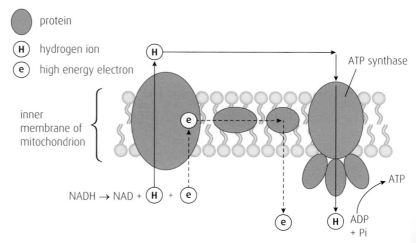

THINGS TO DO AND THINK ABOUT

1   What is the role of dehydrogenase?

EXERCISE AND ENERGY SYSTEMS IN MUSCLE CELLS

DON'T FORGET

Creatine phosphate can only supply phosphate and energy for 10 seconds before it runs out.

LACTATE METABOLISM

ATP is required for muscle contraction. Strenuous exercise means that ATP stocks in muscle cells become depleted, as the demand for oxygen outstrips supply and the electron transfer chain can no longer proceed to meet the muscle's needs. In the absence of oxygen, **lactate metabolism** takes place (see page 33). Here, hydrogen from NADH produced in glycolysis is transferred to pyruvate, resulting in the production of lactate.

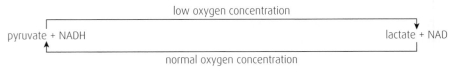

A build up of lactate causes **muscle fatigue**. Once the exercise ceases, the **oxygen debt** that has built up is repaid and lactate is converted back to pyruvic acid and glucose in the liver.

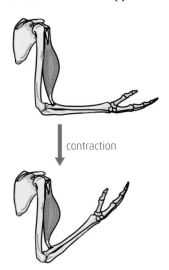

contraction

VIDEO LINK

See a video on slow-twitch and fast-twitch muscle fibres at www.brightredbooks.net

TYPES OF SKELETAL MUSCLE FIBRES

Skeletal muscles move the joints of the skeleton. They are made up of a mixture of slow- and fast-twitch muscle fibres.

Slow-Twitch Muscle Fibres

These are useful for endurance sports, such as cycling and long-distance running. They rely on aerobic respiration to supply their ATP and, as these organelles are the site of aerobic respiration, contain many mitochondria. Additionally, they have a rich blood supply to deliver the oxygen required to maintain an aerobic environment. The fibres contain large quantities of myoglobin. Myoglobin is similar to haemoglobin and is a protein that stores and transports oxygen. The prefix 'myo' means muscle and this protein is only found in muscle. The main source of energy in slow-twitch fibres is **fat**.

Fast-Twitch Muscle Fibres

DON'T FORGET

Fast-twitch muscle fibres have fewer mitochondria and slow-twitch muscle fibres have many mitochondria.

These muscle fibres are needed for sudden bursts of energy, which is required in such sports as the javelin, weight lifting and shot putt, for example. These cells rely on glycolysis to supply their ATP requirements and, as a result, possess fewer mitochondria. They also have fewer blood vessels as they rely only on glycolysis and do not need such an efficient supply of oxygen. Their main sources of energy is **glycogen**.

Athletes will show distinct patterns of muscle fibres that reflect their sporting activities.

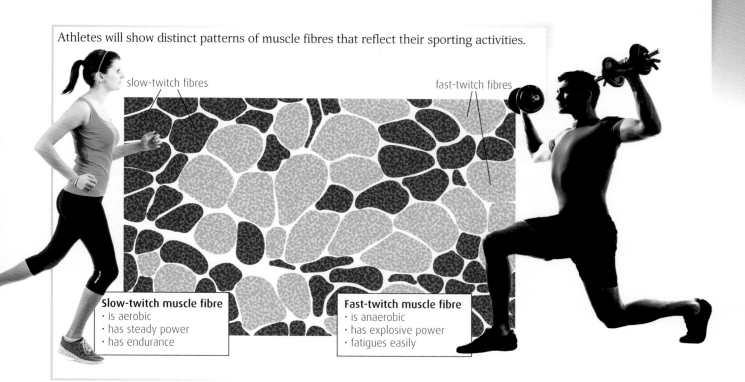

slow-twitch fibres

fast-twitch fibres

Slow-twitch muscle fibre
· is aerobic
· has steady power
· has endurance

Fast-twitch muscle fibre
· is anaerobic
· has explosive power
· fatigues easily

THINGS TO DO AND THINK ABOUT

1   Why are slow-twitch muscle fibres darker than fast-twitch muscle fibres?

2   Predict the ratio of slow-twitch to fast-twitch fibres in a middle-distance runner.

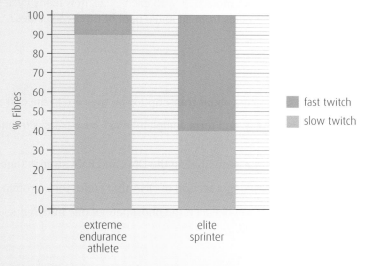

 fast twitch
slow twitch

ONLINE TEST

Head to www.
brightredbooks.net and test
yourself on this topic.

3   Summarise the difference between slow-twitch and fast-twitch muscle fibres.

	Slow-twitch fibres	Fast-twitch fibres
Number of mitochondria		
Blood supply		
Source of energy		
Type of activity		

REVISION QUESTIONS

QUESTION 1

Division by mitosis produces more germline stem cells. Copy the table below and decide if the questions are true or false. If false, correct **the underlined** word.

Statement	True/False	Correction
Somatic stem cells <u>divide</u> by mitosis to form somatic cells.		
<u>Germline</u> stem cells divide by mitosis and by meiosis.		
Division by <u>mitosis</u> produces haploid gametes.		

QUESTION 2

A DNA molecule contained 10 000 nucleotide base pairs. 22% were adenine. How many guanine molecules were present?

QUESTION 3

If PCR doubles the number of DNA molecules with each cycle, how many cycles will be needed to synthesise 1,536 molecules from an initial pool of three molecules?

QUESTION 4

Rearrange the following statements about transcription so they are in the correct order:

   a mRNA nucleotides move in and form complementary base pairs with one of the DNA strands.

   b Weak hydrogen bonds that were holding the DNA and RNA strands together break.

   c RNA Polymerase moves along a section of DNA that codes for a protein.

   d Strong chemical bonds form between the phosphate of one mRNA nucleotide and the ribose sugar of the next.

QUESTION 5

A mutation occurs that leads to the sequence ATCCAGTAC changing to ATCCATAC.

   a What kind of mutation is this?

   b Explain how this would affect the structure of the translated protein.

QUESTION 6

Look at the graph of the effect of substrate concentration on the rate of enzyme reaction.

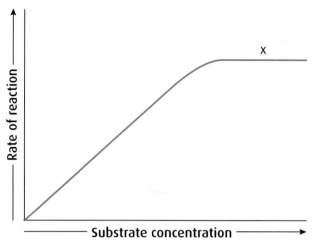

Explain what is happening at point x.

QUESTION 7

a   Describe the action of dehydrogenase enzymes in respiration.

b   What is the benefit of citrate regulating the rate of respiration?

MALE REPRODUCTIVE SYSTEM

The male produces **gametes (sperm cells)** continuously from puberty until death and is said to display **continuous fertility**. This is possible because male sex hormone levels remain constant after puberty.

ORGANS OF THE MALE REPRODUCTIVE SYSTEM

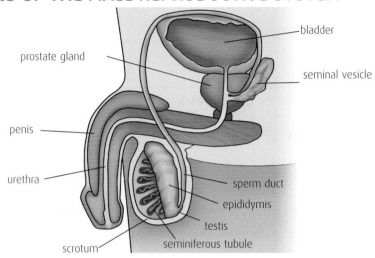

Sperm Production

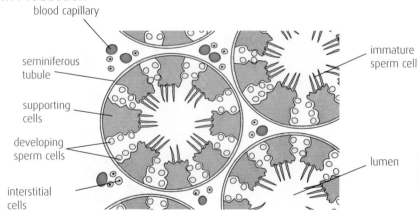

Sperm cells are produced in the **seminiferous tubules** inside the **testes**. These coiled tubes are surrounded by blood vessels and clusters of **interstitial cells** that produce the hormone **testosterone**. Meiosis of **germline cells** in the wall of the seminiferous tubules gives rise to immature sperm cells, which are released by **supporting cells** into the lumen of the seminiferous tubule.

Sperm Cells

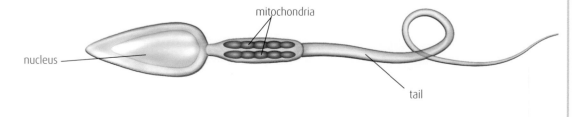

SEMEN

During ejaculation, **semen** passes through the sperm duct and the urethra to be ejected into the female reproductive tract. Semen is a mixture of sperm and secretions from the **seminal vesicles** and **prostate gland**, which maintain the mobility and viability of the sperm. The reproductive glands contribute to semen as follows:

Prostate gland	The prostate gland secretes a milky fluid containing **enzymes** that keep the fluid thin.
Seminal vesicles	The seminal vesicles secrete an alkaline, viscous fluid containing **fructose** and **prostaglandins**. Fructose is a respiratory substrate which provides energy for movement of the sperm tail. Prostaglandins cause the female reproductive tract to contract, helping sperm movement.

HORMONAL CONTROL OF THE MALE REPRODUCTIVE SYSTEM

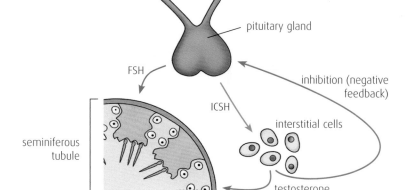

Sperm production is under the control of **follicle stimulating hormone (FSH)** and **interstitial cell stimulating hormone (ICSH)**, two hormones that are released from the pituitary gland in the brain; and testosterone released from the testes.

Follicle stimulating hormone (FSH)	FSH acts on the seminiferous tubules to promote sperm production.
Interstitial cell stimulating hormone (ICSH)	ICSH acts on the interstitial cells of the testes, stimulating the production of **testosterone**.
Testosterone	Testosterone is produced by the interstitial cells in the testes. It acts on the seminiferous tubules, stimulating sperm production and activates the prostate and seminal vesicles.

Overproduction of testosterone is prevented by a **negative feedback** mechanism. When the testosterone level increases above normal, it inhibits secretion of FSH and ICSH from the pituitary. Testosterone production then stops until the level drops below normal, when the inhibitory effect is switched off and production begins again.

 THINGS TO DO AND THINK ABOUT

Sterilisation in the male (vasectomy) involves cutting the sperm duct within the scrotum. What effect would this operation have on (i) the level of testosterone in the blood and (ii) sperm production?

DON'T FORGET

Hormones reach their target organs through the bloodstream.

DON'T FORGET

To bring about the onset of puberty, the pituitary gland is stimulated to produce FSH and ICSH by a releaser hormone from the hypothalamus.

DON'T FORGET

A large number of sperm are needed, as only a tiny fraction will reach the ovum.

ONLINE TEST

Want to test your knowledge of the male reproductive system? Head to www.brightredbooks.net

FEMALE REPRODUCTIVE SYSTEM

The female displays **cyclical fertility** (eggs are produced only once a month) due to changes in hormone levels throughout the menstrual cycle. This continues from puberty to the menopause.

MENSTRUAL CYCLE

The menstrual cycle consists of cyclical changes in both the ovary and the uterus.

Changes in the Ovary

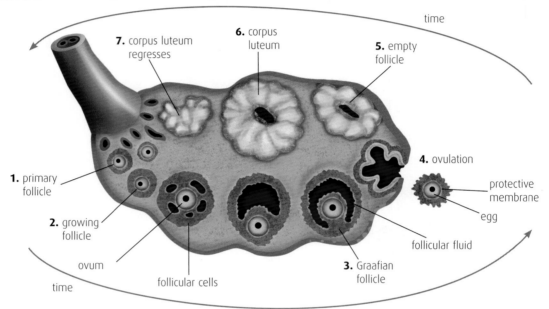

7. corpus luteum regresses

6. corpus luteum

5. empty follicle

time

4. ovulation

protective membrane

egg

1. primary follicle

2. growing follicle

ovum

follicular cells

3. Graafian follicle

follicular fluid

time

Follicular phase	Under the influence of **follicle stimulating hormone (FSH)** from the pituitary gland, **follicles** begin to develop during the **follicular phase**. The follicular cells produce follicular fluid, which gathers within the follicle as it enlarges; and secrete **oestrogen**, which acts on the **pituitary gland**, stimulating the production of **luteinising hormone (LH)**. Usually only one follicle matures fully to produce a **Graafian follicle**. Peak oestrogen level stimulates an **LH surge**. About 10–12 hours later, the Graafian follicle ruptures (causing **ovulation**) on about day 14 of the menstrual cycle, releasing the ovum.
Luteal phase	The ovary now enters the **luteal phase** where, under the influence of LH, the **corpus luteum** develops from the remaining cells of the ruptured follicle. The corpus luteum produces **progesterone** and **oestrogen**, which have a negative-feedback effect on the pituitary gland, inhibiting the release of FSH and preventing development of any more follicles. If no pregnancy occurs, LH, progesterone and oestrogen levels will decrease and the corpus luteum will degenerate, allowing the development of follicles to begin again in the next cycle. If there is a pregnancy, the corpus luteum continues to function until the placenta is large enough to take over hormone production.

Changes in the Uterus

During the menstrual cycle the following changes occur in the uterus:

Menstruation	Low levels of oestrogen and progesterone cause the lining layer of the uterus (**endometrium**) to be shed. The **menstrual flow** consists of a mixture of endometrial cells, mucus, blood and tissue fluid.

contd

Follicular phase	Increasing oestrogen production from the ovarian follicles stimulates repair of the endometrium. The endometrium becomes thicker and develops a good blood supply. Oestrogen also makes the cervical mucus less viscous, allowing sperm to pass through more easily.
Luteal phase	**After ovulation**, the endometrium continues to thicken under the influence of progesterone from the corpus luteum. This is accompanied by further development of the endometrial blood vessels and endometrial glands, preparing the uterus for implantation of the blastocyst, should fertilisation take place. If there is no fertilisation, the drop in progesterone level that results from degeneration of the corpus luteum causes the uterus to enter the next menstrual phase. If fertilisation does occur, the endometrium will be maintained.

DON'T FORGET

If a pregnancy results, the placenta will take over production of progesterone, maintaining the endometrium and preventing miscarriage.

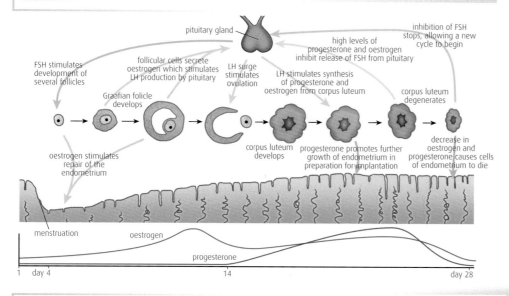

ONLINE

Learn more about ovarian and uterine cycles by following the link at www.brightredbooks.net

FERTILISATION AND IMPLANTATION

If gametes are viable, the following sequence of events can occur after intercourse:

Fertilisation	Sperm usually reach the ovum in the **oviduct**. Here, they release enzymes that enable them to penetrate the layer surrounding the ovum, allowing fertilisation to occur. The fertilised ovum is called a **zygote**. To prevent fertilisation by more than one sperm, the ovum changes the chemical structure of the layers that surround it, making it impossible for other sperm to pass through.
Cleavage	As the zygote travels down the oviduct towards the uterus, it divides by a process called **cleavage** to produce a ball of cells called a **blastocyst**.
Implantation	After about 7 days, implantation takes place, when the blastocyst enters the uterus and embeds in the endometrium.
Differentiation	Embryonic cells now differentiate to produce specialised tissues of the embryo, embryonic components of the placenta and the amniotic sac.

ONLINE TEST

Test your knowledge of the female reproductive system at www.brightredbooks.net

 THINGS TO DO AND THINK ABOUT

The menstrual cycle is under the control of hormones released by both the ovary and the pituitary gland. Make a list of the effects of each of the following hormones on the organs of the female reproductive system:

1 follicle stimulating hormone
2 luteinising hormone
3 oestrogen
4 progesterone.

THE BIOLOGY OF CONTROLLING FERTILITY

BIOLOGICAL BASIS OF CONTRACEPTION

Contraceptive methods act by preventing either fertilisation or implantation. You should, in particular, be familiar with the use of hormonal methods and determination of the fertile period.

Hormonal Methods

The oral contraceptive pill contains a combination of the hormones oestrogen and progesterone. These mimic negative feedback by inhibiting production of FSH and LH from the pituitary gland. As a result, follicles in the ovary do not mature and ovulation does not take place.

The minipill contains progesterone and causes thickening of the cervical mucus.

The morning-after pill acts by preventing ovulation or implantation.

Determination of the Fertile Period

Females may try to prevent conception by avoiding intercourse around the fertile period, when conception is possible. As ova survive for approximately 24 hours after ovulation and sperm can live for about 3 days in the female reproductive tract, the fertile period starts about 3 days before ovulation and ends the day after ovulation.

In the example shown, the menstrual cycle lasts 28 days, with ovulation occurring on day 14. The fertile period starts on day 11, as sperm deposited in the female reproductive tract on this day would still be capable of fertilising the ovum on day 14. Day 15 is the last day of the fertile period as the ovum would not be viable after this day.

ONLINE

For an NHS guide to contraception, see: www.nhs.uk/Conditions/Contraception

The menstrual cycle: about 28 days

bleeding begins

fertile period

ovulation

INFERTILITY AND ITS TREATMENT

For fertilisation and implantation to occur, viable gametes must be produced and the following events must be both possible and coordinated:

- The ovum must be able to travel down the oviduct.
- Sperm must be able to swim through the female reproductive tract to reach and fertilise the ovum.
- The endometrium must be ready to receive the embryo.

About 10% of couples are infertile, with the most common cause being failure to ovulate. You should be familiar with the different causes of infertility and methods that can be used to treat them.

DON'T FORGET

Ovulatory drugs can result in multiple births or can be used to collect ova for IVF.

DON'T FORGET

After ovulation, female body temperature rises approximately 0.5°C and the cervical mucus becomes thin and watery.

ONLINE

Learn more about infertility and the various treatments available at www.brightredbooks.net

Failure to ovulate	This is usually the result of a **hormone imbalance** and is treated by using **fertility drugs** that prevent the negative feedback effect of oestrogen on FSH secretion. Fertility drugs may result in superovulation causing multiple births. Additional ova can be collected for *in vitro* fertilisation.
Low sperm count	A low level of sperm production is often caused by a **hormone imbalance** and can be treated using **testosterone**, *in vitro* **fertilisation, artificial insemination** using donor sperm or intracytoplasmic sperm injection.
Blockage of oviducts	Oviducts can become blocked through **infection** or abnormal tissue growth. Where blockages cannot be surgically removed, *in vitro* **fertilisation** may be an option.
Failure to implant	For implantation to occur, the monthly changes in the endometrium must be synchronised with changes in the ovary, so that the endometrium is thick enough to receive an embryo as it enters the uterus. **Hormone imbalances** can prevent coordination of the ovarian and uterine changes and can be treated using **fertility drugs**.

contd

In Vitro Fertilisation

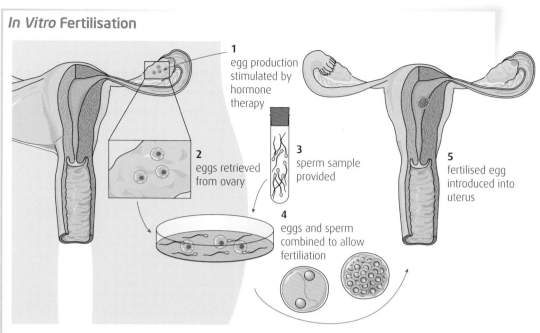

1 egg production stimulated by hormone therapy

2 eggs retrieved from ovary

3 sperm sample provided

4 eggs and sperm combined to allow fertiliation

5 fertilised egg introduced into uterus

This technique involves giving hormones to the female, causing several ova to be released at ovulation. A syringe is inserted into the female's abdominal cavity, allowing the ova to be collected and placed in liquid nutrient. Sperm are either added to the liquid or injected into an ovum, bringing about fertilisation. The fertilised eggs are incubated until they have formed at least eight cells and then several embryos are inserted into the female's uterus.

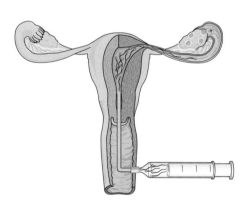

Artificial Insemination

In artificial insemination, semen is collected and inserted into the female reproductive tract using a catheter, without intercourse having taken place. If a male has a low sperm count, multiple samples of his sperm can be combined and then inserted into his partner's reproductive tract to increase the chances of fertilisation. If the male is infertile, semen from a donor can be used to inseminate the female.

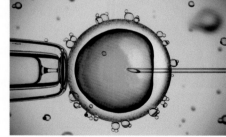

Intracytoplasmic Sperm Injection (ICSI)

If mature sperm are either defective or very low in number, sperm can be collected either after ejaculation or, if this is not possible, directly from the epididymis or testes. A single sperm is selected and the head is injected directly into an egg to achieve fertilisation.

THINGS TO DO AND THINK ABOUT

Barrier methods of contraception work by placing a physical barrier between the sperm and ovum, preventing fertilisation from occurring. Spermicides (chemicals that kill sperm) are often used at the same time as the barrier method, in order to increase its effectiveness. Research the common barrier methods of contraception, such as condoms, cervical cap and diaphragm.

Sterilisation prevents fertilisation by blocking the oviducts (female) or cutting the sperm ducts (male) to prevent sperm from reaching the eggs.

An intrauterine device (IUD) is a small T-shaped plastic and copper device which is placed into the uterus. The copper is toxic to sperm and prevents fertilisation or implantation.

ONLINE TEST

Head to www. brightredbooks.net and test yourself on contraception and infertility.

ANTENATAL AND POSTNATAL SCREENING

At antenatal appointments, a pregnant woman is asked health and family-history questions, and undergoes **screening tests**. This allows calculation of the risk of some disorders, so that – if any problems are indicated – she can be offered **diagnostic tests** to provide a **prenatal diagnosis**. A **genetic counsellor** will discuss any diagnosis with the family.

DON'T FORGET

Screening tests are routinely made for thalassaemia, Down's syndrome and spina bifida, but can also include cystic fibrosis, sickle-cell anaemia and Tay-Sachs disease.

DON'T FORGET

False positive tests can result if substances are measured at the wrong stage of pregnancy.

DON'T FORGET

Antibodies cross the placenta from mother to foetus.

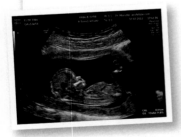

ANTENATAL SCREENING TESTS

Maternal and foetal health **screening tests** include measuring maternal weight, height and blood pressure, as well as monitoring changes in particular chemicals.

Weight and height	Weight and height are measured to calculate body mass index (BMI) as women who are overweight are at greater risk of problems during pregnancy, including gestational diabetes, miscarriage, high blood pressure and pre-eclampsia, and are also more likely to require either an instrumental delivery or a caesarean section.
Blood pressure	High blood pressure (hypertension) affects between 10–15% of pregnancies in the UK. In later pregnancy this can be an indicator of pre-eclampsia.

Biochemical Testing

Biochemical tests are used to chart the normal physiological changes that take place during pregnancy. Blood and urine tests are carried out to monitor concentrations of marker chemicals at particular stages during pregnancy.

Urine is tested for protein. This is an indicator of infection, diabetes or pre-eclampsia.

Blood tests include:
- Rhesus-antibody testing – females who are Rhesus negative and who have not developed anti-D antibodies will be offered anti-D injections at 28 and 34 weeks of pregnancy and also after the birth.
- Anaemia – if anaemic, the female is offered iron and folic acid supplements.

Ultrasound Imaging

In the UK, two ultrasound scans are usually offered. A **dating scan** is made at between 8 and 14 weeks, to allow the gestational age and due date to be determined. An **anomaly scan** is made at between 18 and 20 weeks to detect any physical problems.

Images are produced when high-frequency sound waves travel from a probe (transducer), through gel on the skin, and then bounce back from body organs. The great benefit of ultrasound images is that they can show, not only the structure of the baby's organs, but also their movements and blood flow.

DIAGNOSTIC TESTING

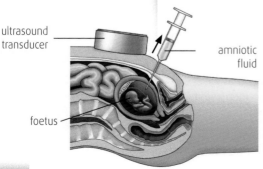

ultrasound transducer

amniotic fluid

foetus

If screening tests, family history or maternal risk category indicate the need for further testing, parents are offered diagnostic testing.

Amniocentesis

A needle is inserted through the wall of the abdomen and uterus, into the amniotic sac, to collect a sample of amniotic fluid. This contains foetal skin and hair cells. The extracted cells are grown in tissue culture before their chromosomes are examined in a karyotype.

Amniocentesis has a low risk of miscarriage (0·5–1% above normal) but cannot be performed until between 16 and 18 weeks of pregnancy, when the mother is beginning to feel an attachment to her unborn child.

contd

Chorionic Villus Sampling (CVS)

A small sample of foetal cells from the placenta is removed, either through the wall of the abdomen or through the vagina. The extracted cells are grown in tissue culture and their chromosomes are examined in a karyotype to diagnose a range of conditions.

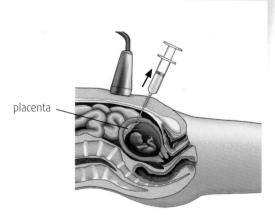

placenta

This test can be carried out at between 8 to 10 weeks. As part of the placenta is being removed, the risk of miscarriage is increased (2–3% above normal). Also, maternal cells may be extracted with the foetal cells, giving a false result.

Karyotyping

Once foetal cells have been obtained, they are grown in tissue culture. Pictures of the foetal chromosomes are taken during mitosis, and a **karyotype** is constructed. The complete foetal chromosome complement is analysed by arranging the homologous pairs of chromosomes in order by **size**, **shape** and **banding pattern**. A genetic counsellor looks for missing, extra or abnormal chromosomes.

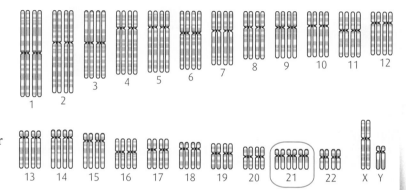

The karyotype here shows Down's syndrome, where there is an extra chromosome number 21.

Pre-implantation Genetic Diagnosis (PGD) in IVF

During *in vitro* fertilisation (IVF) procedures, it is possible to extract embryonic cells for genetic profiling prior to implantation. PGD allows embryos free of specific genetic conditions to be selected for implantation as single gene disorders and chromosomal abnormalities can be detected.

 DON'T FORGET

A karyotype shows an individual's chromosomes arranged as homologous pairs.

POSTNATAL SCREENING

Phenylketonuria (PKU) is an inherited condition caused by a substitution mutation. An enzyme which converts phenylalanine to tyrosine is non-functional, causing a build-up of phenylalanine.

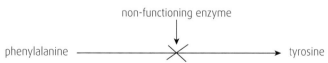

non-functioning enzyme

phenylalanine ————————X————————→ tyrosine

ONLINE

Head to www. brightredbooks.net to see a pregnancy and new-born screening timeline.

If it is not detected and treated very quickly after birth, postnatal development of the brain is affected. Affected individuals must be given a reduced phenylalanine diet. Routine screening for PKU is currently undertaken in the UK after every birth.

THINGS TO DO AND THINK ABOUT

Nuchal Translucency (NT) Scan

This is a screening test which estimates the risk of Down's syndrome and other chromosomal abnormalities using an ultrasound scan at between 11 and 13 weeks plus 6 days, when the foetus is between 45 mm and 84 mm long. The amount of fluid under the skin at the back of the neck (the nuchal translucency) is measured and used, along with maternal age, to determine risk. 75% of babies with Down's syndrome can be detected and the accuracy can be increased by using a combined scan and blood test. If Down's syndrome is indicated, amniocentesis or chorionic villus sampling is offered.

 ONLINE TEST

How well have you learned about antenatal and postnatal screening? Take the test at www. brightredbooks.net

PEDIGREE CHARTS (FAMILY TREES)

Genetic counsellors discuss the family history of inherited disorders with patients. This allows a pedigree chart to be constructed. From the chart, the counsellor determines the pattern of inheritance and calculates the risk of a condition being passed on to the next generation through inherited alleles.

The key below should be used with each of the pedigree charts.

Key

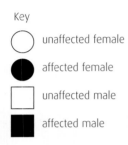

○ unaffected female

● affected female

□ unaffected male

■ affected male

AUTOSOMAL DOMINANT INHERITANCE

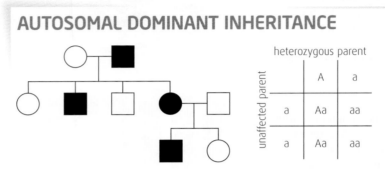

heterozygous parent

unaffected parent	A	a
a	Aa	aa
a	Aa	aa

- Parents who are unaffected have unaffected children.
- Affected individuals with unaffected partners have a 50% chance of having an affected child (see Punnett square above).
- The characteristic is seen in every generation.
- Both sexes are equally affected.

Examples of autosomal dominant conditions are **Huntington's chorea** and **achondroplasia**.

ONLINE

Learn more about autosomal dominant and recessive conditions by following the links at www. brightredbooks.net

AUTOSOMAL RECESSIVE INHERITANCE

affected parent

carrier	a	a
A	Aa	Aa
a	aa	aa

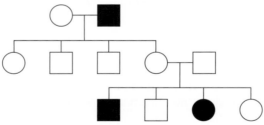

- Parents who are both unaffected but heterozygous can have affected children.
- Children of affected parents always inherit the recessive allele.
- Both sexes are equally affected.
- The condition can skip generations.

Examples of autosomal recessive conditions are **cystic fibrosis** and **PKU**.

carrier

carrier	A	a
A	AA	Aa
a	Aa	aa

SEX-LINKED INHERITANCE

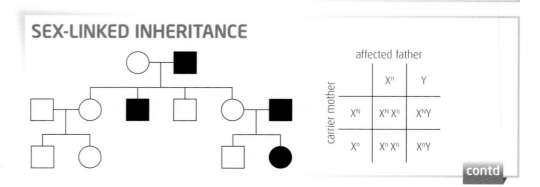

affected father

carrier mother	X^n	Y
X^N	$X^N X^n$	$X^N Y$
X^n	$X^n X^n$	$X^n Y$

contd

- More males than females are affected.
- Only females can be carriers.
- Daughters of affected males are either carriers or affected.
- A carrier with a normal partner has a 50% chance of having an affected son or a carrier daughter.
- The condition can skip generations.

The Punnett square shows the possible genotypes of children whose parents were a carrier female and affected male.

Examples of sex-linked inheritance are **Duchenne muscular dystrophy**, **haemophilia** and **red–green colour blindness**.

INCOMPLETE DOMINANCE INHERITANCE

Where two alleles are **incompletely dominant**, a heterozygous individual will have a phenotype that is a blend of the two homozygous types. An example of incomplete dominance is sickle-cell trait. The gene which codes for haemoglobin has two alleles: allele A codes for normal haemoglobin and allele S codes for haemoglobin S. Unaffected individuals have a genotype AA, and their red blood cells contain normal haemoglobin. The table below shows the other genotypes and phenotypes associated with this gene.

Genotype	Phenotype	Description of condition
SS	sickle-cell anaemia	Individuals who are homozygous for the haemoglobin S allele suffer from sickle-cell anaemia. Haemoglobin S binds with less oxygen than normal haemoglobin. Red blood cells are sickle shaped and clump together, which blocks blood vessels. People with this condition often die at a young age.
AS	sickle-cell trait	Heterozygous individuals suffer a less serious condition called sickle-cell trait. Red blood cells are a normal biconcave shape and contain both normal haemoglobin and haemoglobin S.

In the following example, a woman who has sickle-cell trait and a man who is unaffected have children together. The expected frequency of each phenotype in the first generation is shown.

parents		mother		father
phenotype		sickle-cell trait	×	unaffected
genotype		AS		AA
gametes		A or S		all A

F_1 Punnett square

	A	A
A	AA	AA
S	AS	AS

Offspring genotype	Offspring phenotype	Expected frequency
AA	unaffected	50%
AS	sickle-cell trait	50%

 THINGS TO DO AND THINK ABOUT

Risk Evaluation in Polygenic Inheritance

The disorders described above are all single-gene disorders. Polygenic disorders are caused by more than one gene working in combination. You should be aware that it is more difficult to accurately measure the probability of inheriting a genetic disorder when the condition is polygenic. This is because environmental factors, as well as genes, play a role in determining the severity of the condition. Examples of polygenic disorders include diabetes and asthma.

CARDIOVASCULAR SYSTEM

The cardiovascular system is composed of:

- blood – consisting of red and white blood cells, platelets and plasma.
  The blood transports oxygen and carbon dioxide, food molecules and hormones around the body. It also carries heat around the body. (The liver is responsible for generating most heat when the body is at rest)
- blood vessels – which transport the blood around the body
- the heart – which pumps blood through the vessels.

artery

BLOOD VESSELS

The direction of blood flow through the circulatory system is as follows:

Heart

The heart is the muscular pump which pushes blood around the system.

Artery

Arteries carry blood away from the heart. They have thick walls made of: an outer layer of connective tissue, which contains elastic fibres; a middle layer of smooth muscle with more elastic fibres; an inner lining layer of cells, called the endothelium. Elastic fibres allow the vessel to stretch and recoil to accommodate the surge of blood after each heart contraction. This is what you feel when you take your pulse. The thick muscle layer allows the artery to withstand the high pressure produced by the heart muscle. The smooth muscle can contract to cause vasoconstriction or relax to cause vasodilation. This controls blood flow.

Arteriole

capillary

wall one cell thick

Capillary

Capillaries are the smallest blood vessels and have very thin walls, just one cell thick. As blood flows through a capillary, liquid is forced through the walls by the blood pressure and enters the tissue fluid. The capillaries are so narrow that red blood cells must squeeze through, slowing down the rate of blood flow, giving more time for exchange of materials, and reducing the blood pressure. The blood pressure is, therefore, higher at the arterial end and lower at the venous end where some of the tissue fluid drains back into the capillary to be returned to the heart.

Venule

vein

Vein

Veins carry blood back towards the heart. An endothelium lines the lumen of the vessel. Outside this, lies a much thinner layer of smooth muscle than is found in arteries of similar size (a thicker layer is not needed as the blood is at low pressure). Connective tissue containing elastic fibres forms the outermost layer. Valves are present in the walls to prevent the backflow of blood. Blood flow through the veins is assisted by contraction of muscles in the surrounding tissues, for example in the leg, where contraction of the calf muscles helps to push blood back up the lower limb.

contd

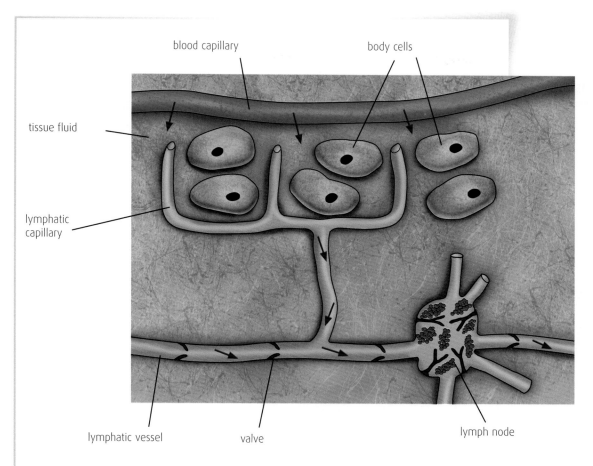

blood capillary

body cells

tissue fluid

lymphatic capillary

lymphatic vessel

valve

lymph node

LYMPHATIC SYSTEM

Most cells in the human body are not in contact with the blood. Instead they are bathed in tissue fluid, which has passed out through the walls of the blood capillaries by pressure filtration. Tissue fluid does not contain plasma proteins as they are too large to pass through capillary walls. It allows exchange of metabolites between tissue cells and the blood. It contains carbon dioxide and other metabolic waste that diffuses out of the body cells to be excreted and supplies body cells with glucose, oxygen and other substances. Much of the tissue fluid drains back into the bloodstream, but some enters blind-ending tubes called **lymphatic capillaries** to form **lymph**. Lymphatic capillaries drain into larger **lymphatic vessels**, which link up to form the lymphatic system. As there is no pump in the lymphatic system (unlike the blood transport system which has the heart), flow of lymph is brought about by contraction of muscles in the surrounding tissues. Valves within the lymphatic vessels prevent backflow of fluid.

The largest lymphatic vessels return lymph to the blood circulatory system by draining into two large veins in the chest (the subclavian veins). As lymph flows through the lymphatic vessels, it passes through swellings called **lymph nodes**. These can be found either singly or accumulated in groups in areas such as the groin and the armpit.

 THINGS TO DO AND THINK ABOUT

1 Explain the function of (a) elastic fibres in artery walls and (b) smooth muscle fibres in arteriole walls.

2 Which blood vessels have valves in their walls? What is their function?

3 In what way are tissue fluid and blood plasma different?

 **DON'T FORGET**

The blood pressure decreases as blood moves away from the heart.

 **DON'T FORGET**

Materials are exchanged between tissue fluid and body cells by pressure filtration.

 VIDEO LINK

Learn more about the cardiovascular system by watching the clip at www.brightredbooks.net

 ONLINE TEST

Head to www.brightredbooks.net and test yourself on the cardiovascular system.

THE HEART

The heart is the muscular organ which pumps blood around the body. It is often referred to as a double pump: the right side of the heart pumps deoxygenated blood to the lungs and the left side of the heart pumps oxygenated blood to all parts of the body.

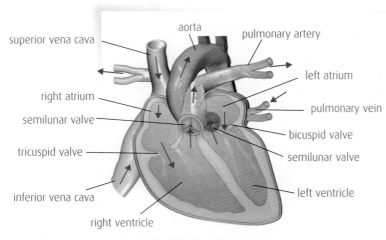

COMPONENTS OF THE HEART

The heart is made up of four chambers: two **atria** that receive blood from the main veins and two **ventricles** that pump blood either to the lungs (right ventricle) or to the body (left ventricle). The heart muscle (cardiac muscle) is supplied by the **coronary arteries**. Valves within the heart are present to prevent backflow of blood.

VIDEO LINK

Watch the animation of blood flow through the human heart at www. brightredbooks.net

Name of valve	Location	Phase of cardiac cycle when valve is closed	Function of valve
Atrioventricular valves (AV) (tricuspid and bicuspid)	Between the atria and ventricles	Ventricular systole	Prevent the backflow of blood into the atria
Semilunar valves (SL)	At the start of the pulmonary artery (on the right) and the aorta (on the left)	Atrial systole	Prevent the backflow of blood from the main arteries into the ventricles

CARDIAC CYCLE

The sequence of filing and emptying of the heart chambers is called the **cardiac cycle**. During the cardiac cycle, contraction and relaxation of cardiac muscle alters the blood pressure within each of the heart chambers, causing the correct flow of blood through the heart. Blood will always flow from high to low blood pressure unless a valve is closed, preventing blood flow. The cardiac cycle is divided into periods of relaxation (**diastole**) and periods of contraction (**systole**).

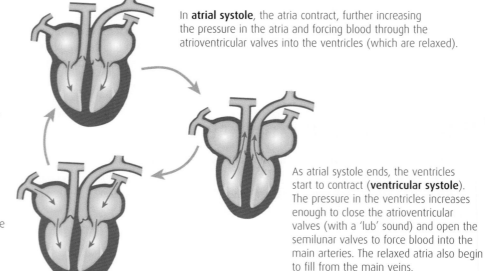

In **atrial systole**, the atria contract, further increasing the pressure in the atria and forcing blood through the atrioventricular valves into the ventricles (which are relaxed).

In **diastole**, the ventricles relax, causing the pressure to drop below that of the main arteries, closing the semilunar valves (with a 'dup' sound). The atria are relaxed and continue to fill with blood from the vena cava and pulmonary vein, increasing the pressure above that of the ventricles. This forces the atrioventricular valves open, and the ventricles begin to fill.

As atrial systole ends, the ventricles start to contract (**ventricular systole**). The pressure in the ventricles increases enough to close the atrioventricular valves (with a 'lub' sound) and open the semilunar valves to force blood into the main arteries. The relaxed atria also begin to fill from the main veins.

CONTROL OF THE CARDIAC CYCLE

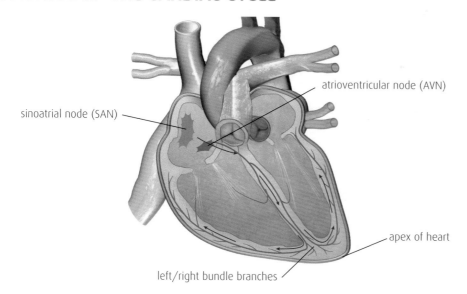

sinoatrial node (SAN)

atrioventricular node (AVN)

apex of heart

left/right bundle branches

DON'T FORGET

The SAN sets the rate at which the heart contracts.

ONLINE

For more on the human heart, follow the link at www.brightredbooks.net

Although cardiac muscle is able to beat on its own, the contraction of each heart chamber must be coordinated to bring about the correct movement of blood.

Coordination of the cardiac cycle is brought about by the **conducting system** of the heart. Electrical excitement (a **cardiac impulse**) is initiated in an area of the wall of the right atrium called the **sinoatrial node (SAN)**, the pacemaker of the heart, where the cells are **auto-rhythmic**. From here, a wave of contraction moves out across the atria (causing atrial systole) to reach the **atrioventricular node (AVN)** in the right atrium. The impulse passes down through a bundle of fibres in the central wall of the heart to reach the apex of the heart, then up through left and right branches to the walls of the ventricles. Ventricular contraction (systole) begins at the apex of the ventricles and spreads upwards to squeeze blood out of the ventricles towards the main arteries.

The heart rate is under both nervous (page 65) and hormonal control.

DON'T FORGET

To follow the cardiac cycle, you only need to consider one side of the heart (as the right side is always at the same stage as the left side).

- **Sympathetic nerves** increase the heart rate.

- A **parasympathetic nerve**, the vagus nerve, decreases the heart rate.

- The **medulla oblongata** in the brain regulates the rate of the SAN through the antagonistic actions of the autonomic nervous system.

- **Noradrenaline (nor-epinephrine)** is released by the sympathetic accelerator nerves and increases the heart rate, and **acetylcholine** – released by parasympathetic nerves – decreases the heart rate.

THINGS TO DO AND THINK ABOUT

Which line in the table correctly identifies the state of the heart valves during ventricular systole?

	Semi-lunar valves	Atrio-ventricular valves
A	open	open
B	open	closed
C	closed	open
D	closed	closed

ONLINE TEST

Test your knowledge of the heart at www.brightredbooks.net

BLOOD PRESSURE AND ELECTROCARDIOGRAMS

BLOOD PRESSURE

Blood pressure is measured using a sphygmomanometer. A cuff is placed around the upper arm and inflated to temporarily stop blood flow through the artery. For manual devices, a stethoscope is used to listen for sounds in the artery as the pressure is slowly released. This allows the practitioner to determine when the pulse is first heard (**systolic pressure**) and then when the sounds stop again (**diastolic pressure**). A typical blood pressure reading for a young adult is 120/80 mm Hg.

Blood Pressure in the Heart

You should remember that blood will always flow from high to low pressure, unless a closed valve prevents this. The diagram below shows the changes in pressure that occur during the cardiac cycle in the left atrium, left ventricle and the aorta.

ONLINE

For more on the cardiac cycle, follow the link at www.brightredbooks.net

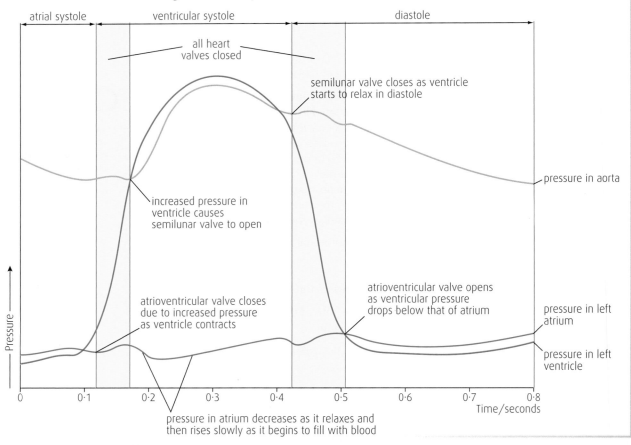

all heart valves closed

semilunar valve closes as ventricle starts to relax in diastole

increased pressure in ventricle causes semilunar valve to open

atrioventricular valve closes due to increased pressure as ventricle contracts

atrioventricular valve opens as ventricular pressure drops below that of atrium

pressure in aorta

pressure in left atrium

pressure in left ventricle

pressure in atrium decreases as it relaxes and then rises slowly as it begins to fill with blood

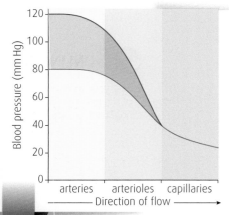

BLOOD PRESSURE IN THE BLOOD VESSEL

In the vessels, blood pressure is caused by the pumping action during contraction and relaxation of the heart ventricles. During ventricular systole, blood pressure is at its highest and it decreases during ventricular diastole. In the arteries, the walls bulge during systole as a wave of blood passes through and recoil during diastole, pushing blood through the vessel. As blood enters narrower vessels, the resistance of the vessel wall increases. This slows blood flow, reducing blood pressure as blood continues travelling along the vessel. The largest decrease in blood pressure takes place in the arterioles, where resistance is at its highest. Blood pressure continues to decrease as blood flows through capillaries, venules and veins.

INTERPRETATIONS OF ELECTROCARDIOGRAMS (ECG)

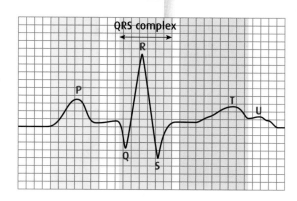

An electrocardiogram records the electrical impulses that are generated in the heart during contraction and relaxation of the cardiac muscle. It is shown on graph paper as a wave. ECGs can indicate various abnormalities, including damage due to a heart attack, abnormal rhythms (arrhythmia) and high blood pressure.

- The P wave is caused by firing of the sinoatrial node, with a wave of electrical activity crossing the atria causing atrial systole.

- Firing of the atrioventricular node produces the QRS complex and initiates the ventricular systole, with electrical activity spreading through the ventricles.

- The T wave results from the AVN recovering. The ventricles return to their resting electrical state (diastole).

DON'T FORGET

The volume of blood pumped by left and right ventricles is equal.

CARDIAC OUTPUT

The **cardiac output** (CO) is the volume of blood pumped through each ventricle per minute. To calculate this, two values must be known:

- **heart rate** (HR) – the number of contractions in one minute

- **stroke volume** (SV) – the volume of blood pumped out by one ventricle during systole.

The following equation is used to calculate cardiac output:

CO = HR × SV

DON'T FORGET

Hypertension (high blood pressure) is a major risk factor for coronary heart disease.

For example, if an individual has a heart rate of 70 beats per minute and a stroke volume of 0·08 litres, then:

CO = 70 × 0·08 = 5·6 l/min

THINGS TO DO AND THINK ABOUT

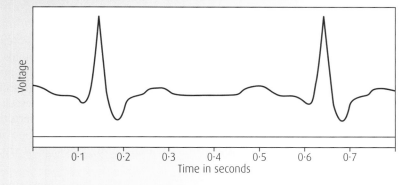

How to calculate the heart rate shown on the electrocardiogram (ECG):

Find the time taken for one heartbeat by identifying the time between two identical points on the graph, e.g. 0·1 and 0·6 seconds; so, it takes 0·5 seconds for one heartbeat. Every second there will be two heartbeats, giving a heart rate of:

2 × 60 = 120 beats per minute

ONLINE TEST

Revise your knowledge of blood pressure and electrocardiograms by taking the topic test at www.brightredbooks.net

PATHOLOGY OF CARDIOVASCULAR DISEASE (CVD) 1

ATHEROSCLEROSIS

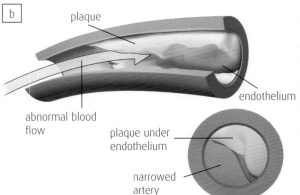

a

artery wall

normal blood flow

artery cross-section

b

plaque

abnormal blood flow

endothelium

plaque under endothelium

narrowed artery

A normal artery (a) and one with atherosclerosis (b)

In **atherosclerosis** the normally smooth wall of the blood vessel (diagram a) becomes roughened by the development of an **atheroma** or **plaque** below the endothelium (diagram b). The atheroma is composed of fibrous material, calcium and fatty materials, including cholesterol. The atheroma gradually gets bigger, causing the artery wall to thicken and the diameter of the lumen to decrease and lose its elasticity. As a result, less blood flows through the vessel – eventually it may block completely. Blood pressure also increases.

Risk factors which can make individuals more likely to develop an atheroma include lack of exercise, a high fat diet, obesity, diabetes and high blood pressure.

Thrombosis

Thrombosis is the formation of a clot (**thrombus**) within a blood vessel. This can be initiated by rupture of an atheroma, causing damage to the endothelium. When this happens, clotting factors activate a chain (a cascade) of linked reactions that convert the inactive enzyme **prothrombin** to the active enzyme, **thrombin**. Part of the cascade is shown below.

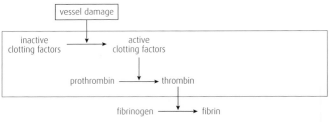

vessel damage

inactive clotting factors → active clotting factors

prothrombin → thrombin

fibrinogen → fibrin

Thrombin is the enzyme which catalyses the conversion of the soluble plasma protein **fibrinogen** into insoluble threads of **fibrin**. As the threads are formed, a mesh builds up which gives a scaffold for scar tissue formation, trapping blood cells and platelets, and forming a **clot**. Sometimes, the thrombus breaks free from its site of formation (forming an **embolus**) and travels around in the blood until it lodges in a smaller blood vessel, blocking blood flow. If either a thrombus or embolus blocks blood flow in an artery, the tissue that the vessel supplies is deprived of oxygen and the cells will die. Blockage of the coronary artery can cause a heart attack (myocardial infarction, **MI**); blockage of arteries in the brain can cause a **stroke**.

Peripheral Vascular Disorders

Where atherosclerosis affects arteries other than those of the brain and heart, the disease is referred to as a **peripheral vascular disorder**. A progressive narrowing of the arteries, most often in the legs, reduces the oxygen supply to the muscles. During exercise, the muscle cells cannot obtain enough oxygen, resulting in pain in the calves and thighs. The poor blood flow can also cause cold and painful fingers and toes.

DON'T FORGET

Atherosclerosis is the major risk factor for many cardiovascular diseases, including angina, heart attack, stroke and peripheral vascular disease.

ONLINE

Learn more about atherosclerosis by following the link at www.brightredbooks.net

contd

Deep vein thrombosis (DVT) results from the production of a blood clot in one of the deep veins. This most frequently occurs in the legs, where slowed blood circulation during long periods of inactivity – either through sitting down (in which case the veins behind the knee joint become kinked) or lying in bed – can add to the effects of atherosclerosis. If an embolus breaks free from the DVT, it can travel to the lung, causing a blockage to one of the pulmonary vessels (a **pulmonary embolism**).

ONLINE TEST

Test yourself on the pathology of cardiovascular disease at www. brightredbooks.net

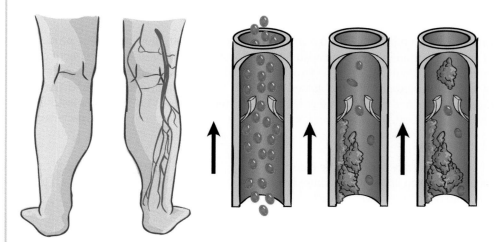

deep veins of the leg · normal blood flow · deep vein thrombosis · embolus

Thrombolytic Medications

Some 'clot busting' drugs, such as **streptokinase** and **tissue plasminogen activator**, can be used for the immediate treatment of stroke, heart attack, DVT and pulmonary embolism. Plasminogen is activated by these drugs, producing plasmin which dissolves fibrin and makes the blood clot soluble.

 THINGS TO DO AND THINK ABOUT

1   Using your knowledge of the pathology of cardiovascular diseases, make a bullet point list of 10 important facts on the occurrence of cardiovascular disease.

2   Which of the following is not a risk factor for atherosclerosis?

   a   high blood pressure

   b   diet rich in fat

   c   exercise

   d   diabetes

3   The conversion of soluble fibrinogen to insoluble fibrin is catalysed by:

   a   active clotting factors

   b   cholesterol

   c   thrombin

   d   prothrombin

PATHOLOGY OF CARDIOVASCULAR DISEASE (CVD) 2

ONLINE

Learn more about high cholesterol at www. brightredbooks.net

CHOLESTEROL

Cholesterol is a type of lipid and a vital substance in the body. It is used in the production of steroid hormones, such as testosterone and oestrogen, and is also a component of cell membranes. About 25% of cholesterol is produced in the liver, but all cells are capable of its synthesis. About 15% is obtained in the diet from the saturated fats found in meat, dairy products and egg yolk. A diet high in saturated fats raises the blood cholesterol level. This, in itself, is not a disease but can lead to the development of atherosclerosis.

Lipoproteins

Cholesterol is transported in the blood by molecules called lipoproteins. These are made up of an outer layer consisting of phospholipids and some proteins. Lying in the centre of the lipoprotein are fats and steroids, including cholesterol.

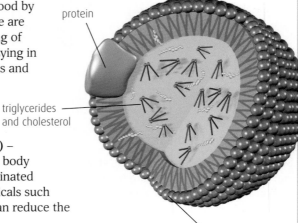

protein

triglycerides and cholesterol

phospholipid monolayer

The two main groups of lipoproteins are:

DON'T FORGET

High HDL levels reduce the chance of developing atherosclerosis.

- **High-density lipoprotein (HDL)** – this transports cholesterol from body cells to the liver, where it is eliminated by breakdown into useful chemicals such as bile salts. A high HDL level can reduce the blood cholesterol level.

- **Low-density lipoprotein (LDL)** – this transports cholesterol from the liver to body cells. A high LDL level can increase the blood cholesterol level.

Role of Lipoprotein in CVD

The extracellular side of the cell membrane contains LDL receptors. When LDL binds to receptors, endocytosis takes place; LDL enters the cell within a vesicle. The vesicle binds to lysosomes and LDL is broken down to produce amino acids and cholesterol. These are released into the cytoplasm of the cell.

Cholesterol, once released into the cytoplasm, suppresses the enzyme which controls the rate of cholesterol biosynthesis (negative feedback), turning off cholesterol synthesis in the cell. It also turns off the synthesis of LDL receptors and prevents any more LDL from entering the cell. As the cell can no longer take in LDL, this circulates in the blood. Cholesterol may be deposited in the arteries, adding to atheromas.

The ratio of HDL to LDL is extremely important in influencing the occurrence of atherosclerosis:

- A high HDL:low LDL ratio results in a lower blood cholesterol level, reducing the chance of developing atherosclerosis.

- A low HDL:high LDL ratio results in a higher blood cholesterol level, increasing the chance of developing atherosclerosis.

contd

Protective Measures

Several lifestyle choices can lead to a high LDL:low HDL ratio and, therefore, increase the cholesterol level in the blood. Smoking, obesity, lack of exercise, and a diet high in saturated fats are all risk factors. By modifying your lifestyle through regular exercise and not smoking, the level of HDL in the blood can be increased. Replacing saturated animal fats in the diet with unsaturated fats also helps to decrease the level of LDL in the blood.

If altering diet and taking exercise do not reduce cholesterol level, drugs such as statins can be prescribed. Statins work by blocking the enzyme in liver cells that catalyses the formation of cholesterol. As the liver cells now cannot make their own cholesterol, they increase the number of LDL receptors on their cell membranes, resulting in more LDL being taken into the cell and reducing the blood cholesterol level. Patients are advised to take statins in the evening because this enzyme is more active at night.

ONLINE TEST

Head to www. brightredbooks.net to test yourself on the pathology of cardiovascular disease.

THINGS TO DO AND THINK ABOUT

1 Match the terms in column A to the definition in column B

Column A		Column B	
(i)	Atheroma	(a)	Blood clot that has broken free and lodged in a blood vessel in the lung.
(ii)	Fibrin	(b)	Caused by blockage of a coronary artery.
(iii)	Stroke	(c)	Plaque composed of fibrous and fatty material which forms under the endothelium
(iv)	DVT		
(v)	High-density lipoproteins	(d)	Substance which transports cholesterol from the liver to body cells
(vi)	Myocardial infarction	(e)	Substance which, if present at high concentration in the blood, is a risk factor for atherosclerosis
(vii)	Pulmonary embolus	(f)	Substance which converts fibrinogen to fibrin
(viii)	Cholesterol	(g)	Substance which transports cholesterol from the body cells to the liver
(ix)	Thrombin	(h)	Caused by formation of a blood clot in the deep veins of the leg
(x)	Low-density lipoproteins	(i)	Insoluble fibres which form a mesh during scar-tissue formation
		(j)	Paralysis caused by blockage of blood vessels in the brain

2 In the table, identify the correct relationship between the ratio of HDL:LDL in the blood, blood cholesterol level and the risk of atherosclerosis.

	Blood cholesterol level	HDL:LDL ratio	Chance of atherosclerosis
A	Low	Low HDL:high LDL	Increased
B	Low	High HDL:low LDL	Lowered
C	High	Low HDL:high LDL	Lowered
D	High	High HDL:low LDL	Increased

3 Which of the following is true of lipoproteins?

a HDL transports cholesterol from the liver to body cells.

b A high concentration of HDL can increase blood cholesterol levels.

c A high HDL: low LDL ratio increases the chances of developing atherosclerosis.

d A low HDL: high LDL ratio results in a higher blood cholesterol level.

4 Which of the following is true of cholesterol?

a The presence of cholesterol in the cytoplasm of body cells can increase the rate of synthesis of more cholesterol.

b It is transported on the outside of lipoproteins.

c The presence of cholesterol in a cell can increase the rate of synthesis of LDL receptors.

d Cholesterol is a component of an atheroma.

BLOOD GLUCOSE LEVEL AND DIABETES

REGULATION OF BLOOD GLUCOSE LEVEL

Carbohydrates obtained in the diet are broken down into glucose. Glucose is used by body cells as the main respiratory substrate and a constant supply is required to give energy in the form of ATP. Homeostatic mechanisms normally maintain blood glucose at a relatively constant level, through a negative-feedback loop. This promotes storage of glucose in the liver when there is excess in the blood and stimulates release of glucose by the liver into the blood as body cells use it up in respiration. This regulation is brought about by the actions of the pancreatic hormones, insulin and glucagon, as shown in the table.

Hormone	Produced in response to	Effect
Insulin	Increased blood glucose concentration after eating a meal	Liver cells respond by converting glucose into glycogen – blood glucose level decreases
Glucagon	Decreased blood glucose concentration between meals	Liver cells respond by converting glycogen into glucose – blood glucose level increases

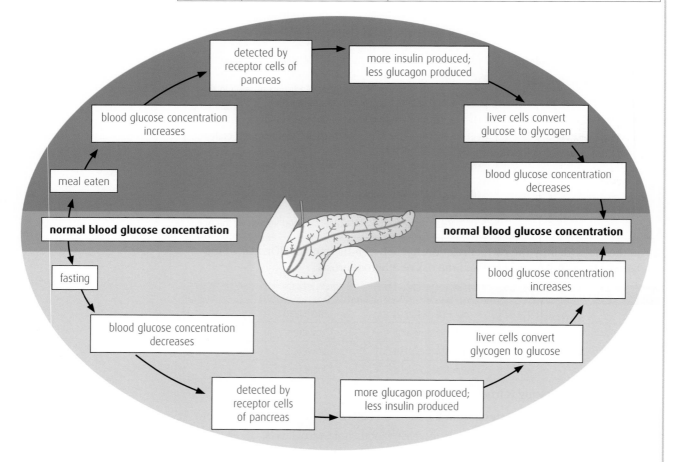

In addition, during periods of exercise and in the 'flight-or-fight' response, glucagon secretion is stimulated and insulin secretion is inhibited by the production of adrenaline from the adrenal glands. This provides muscles with the glucose they require for increased activity.

In type 1 diabetes, this homeostatic mechanism breaks down – insulin production either stops or is decreased, causing the blood glucose level to remain at an elevated level (hyperglycaemia). With elevated blood glucose level, more glucose enters endothelial cells than normal, causing the cells to malfunction and damaging blood vessels.

contd

Over time, atherosclerosis can develop in arteries (macrovascular disease). When small blood vessels are damaged, microvascular disease may occur, affecting the:

- retina – damaged blood vessels may haemorrhage causing blood to leak out and scar tissue to form, blocking vision and leading to blindness

- kidneys – leaky blood vessels allow protein to be excreted with the urine; prolonged damage causes blood vessels to collapse and kidney failure occurs

- peripheral nerves – damage to the nerves of the lower leg and foot (which detect temperature, pressure, and pain) causes numbness. This can allow damage to the area to go unnoticed, with skin ulcers and infection leading to possible gangrene and amputation.

A diabetes diagnosis is made using a **glucose tolerance test**. Here, the individual fasts for 8 hours before drinking between 250 and 300 ml of glucose solution. The blood glucose level is then measured over the next 2 hours. A graph showing the results of a glucose tolerance test is given below.

- In an individual with normal glucose metabolism, the glucose level rises after consumption and then falls rapidly as insulin is produced.

- People with **mild diabetes** have a relatively normal fasting blood glucose level. However after consumption, glucose level becomes much higher than in the normal individual and falls to the fasting level during the test period but at a low rate.

- In **severe diabetes**, fasting blood glucose level is much higher than normal. After consumption, it increases further and does not return to fasting level during the test.

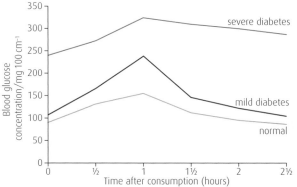

Type of diabetes	Onset	Physiology and treatment
Type 1 diabetes	Usually in childhood	The pancreas does not produce any insulin. As a result, blood glucose level must be measured regularly and the correct amount of insulin injected.
Type 2 diabetes	Usually in adulthood; often in overweight individuals	The pancreas does produce insulin, but the cells have become resistant to it. Insulin resistance results from a decrease in the number of insulin receptors on the membranes of liver, muscle and fat cells. Binding between insulin and its receptor is important as it initiates movement of glucose transporters from an intracellular pool to the cell membrane, allowing glucose to pass into the cell. A decrease in the number of receptors, therefore, results in less glucose entering the cell.

In both types of diabetes, the kidneys will remove some of the blood glucose resulting in glucose appearing in the urine. Tests on the urine for presence of glucose are often used to discover if a person has diabetes.

THINGS TO DO AND THINK ABOUT

The diagram shows some of the stages in the control of blood glucose level.

1. increase in blood glucose level detected

2. hormone X released

3. glucose converted to substance Y

4. blood glucose level decreases

1 In which organ would the increase in blood glucose level be detected?
2 Name hormone X and substance Y.
3 Where does stage 3 occur?
4 If hormone X was not present, the blood glucose level would still drop but very slowly. Explain why it would decrease.

OBESITY

OVERVIEW

In obesity there is an excess of body fat compared to muscle (lean body tissue), which is indicated by a body mass index (BMI) of greater than 30 kg/m².

Obesity increases the chances of developing cardiovascular disease (CVD) and type 2 diabetes. It is caused mainly by:

- a high calorie diet – fats contain twice the energy of carbohydrates and proteins per gram, and sugary foods are digested without any metabolic energy input

- lack of exercise – a sedentary lifestyle reduces energy expenditure.

The modern lifestyle in Western societies, including the UK, has resulted in an increase in the incidence of obesity. Treatment is primarily through dieting and exercise.

A graph titled "Incidence of adult obesity in UK" (y-axis, 10% to 25%) against Year (x-axis, 1994 to 2006), showing two lines labelled "males" and "females" both increasing over time.

VIDEO LINK

Watch the clip at www.brightredbooks.net for more on underwater weighing.

DON'T FORGET

Exercise helps reduce the risk factors for CVD by keeping weight under control, minimising stress and reducing hypertension.

DON'T FORGET

A healthy diet is also important in reducing the risk of obesity and CVD.

DON'T FORGET

Regular exercise can increase the HDL:LDL ratio, which also lowers the risk of CVD (see page 56).

BODY MASS INDEX

A body mass index (BMI) table is used to categorise an individual on a scale ranging from underweight to severely obese. BMI is calculated using the following equation:

$$ \text{BMI} = \frac{\text{mass (kg)}}{\text{height}^2 \ (\text{m}^2)} $$

A BMI of 25–30 indicates a moderate risk of developing CVD, high blood pressure or type 2 diabetes. The risk is greatly increased in obesity, where the BMI increases above 30.

Although BMI is simple to calculate, it can give a poor indication of risk; individuals with a high body mass due to lean tissue (such as body builders) have a BMI which incorrectly indicates that they are overweight.

EFFECTS OF EXERCISE ON THE BODY COMPOSITION

Regular aerobic exercise (such as jogging, swimming or cycling) which increases the heart rate to between 55% and 70% of the maximum (220 – age) maintains a healthy lifestyle. This has important benefits through:

- increasing energy expenditure relative to energy intake, leading to loss of body fat

- increasing and maintaining lean muscle tissue and therefore increasing the muscle:fat ratio

- increasing the basal metabolic rate (BMR), as muscle has a higher metabolic rate than fat tissue.

THINGS TO DO AND THINK ABOUT

1   The graph below shows the incidence of obesity in children from 1971 to 2000.
Describe two trends that can be observed from the graph.

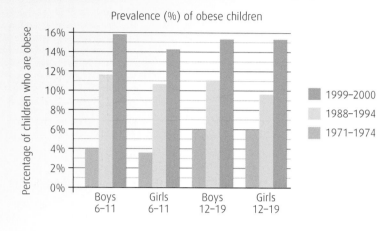

Prevalence (%) of obese children

2   Which of the following is true of the effects of exercise?

a   Regular aerobic exercise increases energy expenditure relative to energy intake.

b   Regular aerobic exercise decreases the muscle:fat ratio.

c   Regular aerobic exercise causes a decrease in the basal metabolic rate.

d   Regular aerobic exercise is a risk factor for DVT.

3   The table below shows the height and mass of four individuals.

Individual	Height (cm)	Mass (kg)
Untrained male	170	65.0
Male athlete	180	105.0
Untrained female	168	82.4
Female athlete	177	91.5

a   Calculate the BMI of each individual.

b   Explain why the untrained female would be more likely to be advised to go on a
reduced calorie diet than the female athlete, although they have a similar BMI.

REVISION QUESTIONS

QUESTION 1

The graph shows hormonal changes in the female reproductive system over a 28-day period.

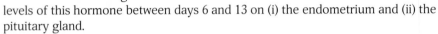

a Identify hormones W, X, Y, and Z.

b Which cells secrete hormone X? Describe the effect of increasing levels of this hormone between days 6 and 13 on (i) the endometrium and (ii) the pituitary gland.

c Which event is stimulated by the surge in hormone Y seen at day 14?

d Which structure forms in the ovary during the luteal phase? Which hormone is secreted by this structure?

e Describe the effect of negative feedback of the ovarian hormones on the pituitary gland.

QUESTION 2

a Match each example situation with the most appropriate method to treat infertility.

Example situation	Methods to treat infertility
1. The male has a low sperm count	a. Ovulatory drugs
2. The sperm are defective or very low in number	b. *In vitro* fertilisation
3. A hormone imbalance results in no ova being produced	c. Artificial insemination
4. The oviducts have become blocked	d. Intracytoplasmic sperm injection

b The oral contraceptive pill is a chemical method of contraception. Describe its effect on the pituitary gland.

QUESTION 3

The diagram below shows the inheritance of Hunter syndrome, a sex-linked condition which causes abnormalities to the respiratory system and the heart. The allele for Hunter syndrome (h) is recessive to the normal allele (H).

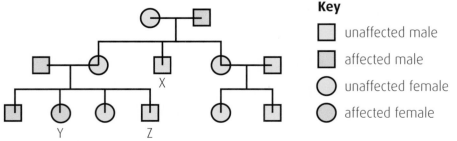

Key

☐ unaffected male

☐ affected male

○ unaffected female

○ affected female

a State the genotypes of individuals X, Y and Z.

b Individual Z has a daughter who is heterozygous for this condition.

  i What is the daughter's genotype?

  ii What term is used to describe females who are heterozygous for sex-linked conditions?

c Name two other conditions which show this type of inheritance pattern.

QUESTION 4

The diagram shows part of the body's transport system.

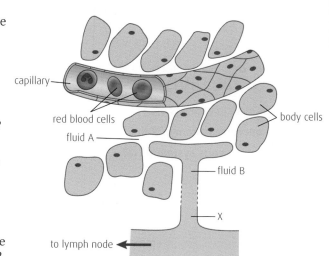

a   Name fluid A, fluid B, and vessel X.

b   How are materials exchanged between fluid A and body cells?

c   Which molecules are found in blood plasma but are missing from fluid A? Why?

d   Which structures located in the vessels assist with ensuring the correct flow of fluid B?

e   What causes the flow of fluid B through the vessels?

QUESTION 5

The graph below shows the results of a glucose tolerance test.

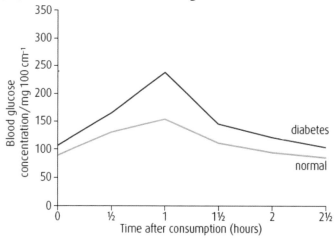

a   Into which storage carbohydrate in the liver is glucose converted?

b   Where is the site of the receptors which detect blood glucose levels?

c   The diabetic individual shown in the graph has type 2 diabetes.

   i   Explain why the blood glucose level rises to a higher level than normal after taking the glucose drink.

   ii   Explain why the blood glucose level in this patient begins to fall after one hour.

d   IWhich hormone would cause glucose to be released from the liver into the blood during periods of exercise?

NEUROBIOLOGY AND IMMUNOLOGY

DIVISIONS OF THE NERVOUS SYSTEM

STRUCTURAL DIVISIONS OF THE NERVOUS SYSTEM

The nervous system consists of:

- **central nervous system** (CNS) – brain and spinal cord
- **peripheral nervous system** (PNS) – peripheral nerves.

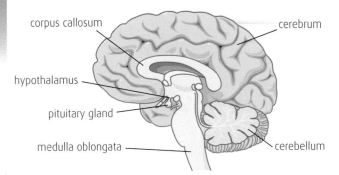

corpus callosum

cerebrum

hypothalamus

pituitary gland

medulla oblongata

cerebellum

THE CENTRAL NERVOUS SYSTEM (CNS)

The central nervous system consists of the brain and spinal cord, and contains neurons (cell bodies, axons and dendrites) and their supporting cells (glial cells).

The Brain

The table shows the parts of the brain with which you should be familiar.

Part of brain	Function
Cerebrum	Involved with conscious activities, such as sensation. Also recalls memories and alters behaviour in light of experience. The left cerebral hemisphere receives sensory information from the right side of the body, including the visual field, and controls the right side of the body.
Cerebellum	Part of the central core of the brain, the cerebellum coordinates contraction of skeletal muscles and controls balance, posture and movement.
Medulla oblongata	Part of the central core, the medulla oblongata controls essential body processes, such as breathing, heart rate, arousal and sleep.
Hypothalamus	The hypothalamus is important in maintaining homeostasis and for regulating basic drives, such as sexual behaviour, drinking and eating.
Limbic system	The limbic system is involved in processing information for memories and influencing emotional and motivational states.

ONLINE

Learn more about the brain by following the link at www.brightredbooks.net

Cerebrum

The cerebrum consists of two cerebral hemispheres (left and right) that are connected by a bridge of nerve fibres called the **corpus callosum**. The corpus callosum is the only route of communication between the hemispheres. The surface of the cerebrum is folded, allowing more cell bodies to be present and maximising the number of connections between neurons.

Functional Areas of the Cerebrum

somatosensory area

motor area

language area

language area

auditory area

visual area

Somatosensory area: receives sensory information from the internal organs, skin and muscles. Parts of the body can be mapped out along the somatosensory area, with body parts that experience fine sensation (such as the lips and fingertips) having a larger area of the cerebrum.

Motor area: controls the contraction of specific muscles. Just like the somatosensory area, the parts of the body are organised along the motor area. Where muscles require fine control (such as muscles of the lips, tongue and fingers), they take up a greater proportion of the motor area. A **motor homunculus** can be drawn to show the relative size of the motor area that controls each part of the body.

Visual area: receives information from the eyes through the optic nerves. Interprets colour, shape and movement.

Association areas: concerned with language, personality, imagination and intelligence.

Language areas: involved with controlling muscles required for speech (muscles of the lips, tongue and larynx) and memory of vocabulary.

Auditory area: receives information from the cochlea in the inner ear, through the auditory nerve. Interprets both pitch and rhythm.

FUNCTIONAL DIVISIONS OF THE PERIPHERAL NERVOUS SYSTEM

The peripheral nervous system can be divided into two functional parts.

1 Somatic Nervous System (SNS)

The **somatic nervous system** contains sensory and motor neurons and is responsible for:

- voluntary control of skeletal muscles
- involuntary reflexes.

2 Autonomic Nervous System (ANS)

The **autonomic nervous system** regulates the internal environment (for example, heart rate, body temperature and digestion). It has two divisions: **sympathetic** and **parasympathetic**. These perform opposing functions (and are, therefore, **antagonistic**), the sympathetic division preparing the body for action and the parasympathetic division returning the body to the resting state. For example, sympathetic nerves speed up the breathing rate and the heart rate, while a parasympathetic nerve (the vagus nerve) slows down the breathing rate and the heart rate (see page 51). Similarly, sympathetic nerves slow down the rate of peristalsis and production of intestinal secretions, and parasympathetic nerves speed up the rate of peristalsis and cause an increase in the production of intestinal secretions once the period of excitement is over.

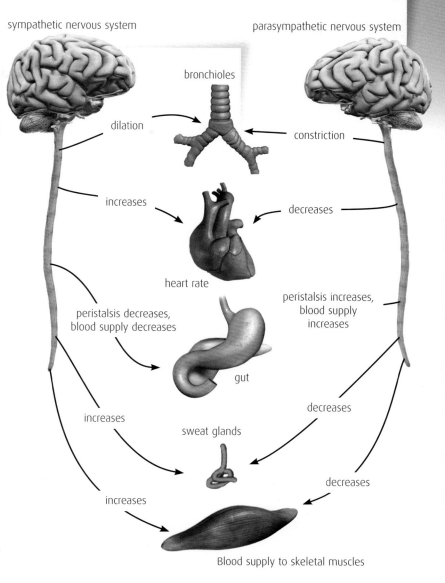

sympathetic nervous system   parasympathetic nervous system

bronchioles

dilation — constriction

increases — decreases

heart rate

peristalsis decreases, blood supply decreases — peristalsis increases, blood supply increases

gut

increases — decreases

sweat glands

increases — decreases

Blood supply to skeletal muscles

THINGS TO DO AND THINK ABOUT

In split-brain patients, the **corpus callosum** is cut, often to reduce epileptic seizures, but preventing transfer of information between the right and left sides of the cerebrum. To understand the effect that this has on the patient, we must remember:

- Visual information in the left field of view is projected onto the right visual cortex, and information in the right field of view is projected onto the left visual cortex.
- The left motor cortex controls muscles on the right side of the body, and the right motor cortex controls muscles on the left side of the body.
- The speech area is usually found only on the left cerebral hemisphere.

In the experiment shown here, a picture of a ball is in the left field of view and a cube is in the right field of view. If asked what can be seen, the patient will say 'cube', as this is projected to the left hemisphere – communication between left visual area and speech area takes place. They cannot say 'ball' because communication between the right and left hemispheres has been cut.

If asked to use the left hand to pick up the ball or the cube from several hidden under a cloth, they would pick up the ball (communication between right visual and motor areas takes place) but wouldn't be able to tell you what they were holding.

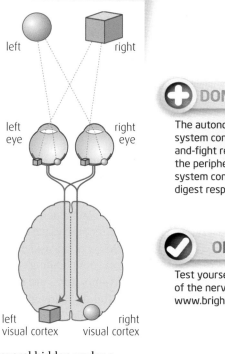

left   right

left eye   right eye

left visual cortex   right visual cortex

DON'T FORGET

The autonomic nervous system controls flight-and-fight responses and the peripheral nervous system controls rest and digest responses.

ONLINE TEST

Test yourself on divisions of the nervous system at www.brightredbooks.net

MEMORY

Memory involves all the processes that enable us to store, retain and retrieve information about sensations and emotions. Memories include past experiences, knowledge and thoughts.

To form new memories, information coming into the brain is changed into a usable form (**encoded**) and **stored**. There must also be a method for **retrieval**, so that we can access the information at a later date.

DON'T FORGET

Shallow encoding results from repetition and elaborative encoding results when information is linked to previous memories.

ENCODING

During **encoding**, information that we see, hear, think and feel is changed into a form that can be stored as a memory. Encoding can be by:

- **acoustic code** – a sound image is created
- **visual code** – a visual image is created.

Storage

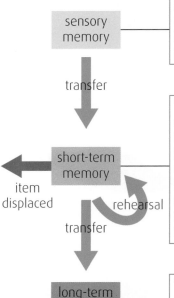

Information coming into the brain from the senses is stored very briefly (for between 0·5 and 3 seconds) in the sensory memory. Only a very limited amount of information from the sensory memory is retained and passed on to the next level of memory: short-term memory.

This is the working memory and consists of information of which we are consciously aware. Short-term memory holds only a small amount of information (**7 ± 2 items**) for up to **30 seconds**. To prevent loss of information from the short-term memory, we can use **rehearsal** (repeating the information). Rehearsal helps with transfer of information into the next memory level: long-term memory. Information that is organised into categories during encoding has a greater chance of being transferred to the long-term memory. Information that is not transferred to the long-term memory will be lost (**displaced**).

The long-term memory has an unlimited capacity and stores information outside our conscious awareness for a long period of time. Information is grouped by type of memory (facts or skills for example).

Short-Term Memory (STM)

DON'T FORGET

The STM can perform simple cognitive tasks (working memory model).

The short-term memory span is 7 ± 2 items. However, we can boost memory by putting related information into groups (**chunking**), forming larger meaningful items that can be stored. For example, the letters and numbers ITV1BBCCH4CH5ITV2MTV form 20 items if taken individually but if we chunk them to get ITV1-BBC-CH4-CH5-ITV2-MTV they form six meaningful items that can be memorised.

Rehearsal is used to aid transfer of information from short-term to long-term memory. Its role can be demonstrated using the **serial position effect**. An experiment to look at this effect is carried out as follows:

1 Subjects are asked to put pens and pencils down before the items are revealed (to prevent cheating).
2 Twenty items are shown, one at a time, each for 5 seconds (limiting rehearsal time).
3 After all 20 items have been shown, subjects write down as many as they can recall.
4 The experiment is repeated with a fresh set of items (to increase reliability).

DON'T FORGET

Rehearsal is a shallow form of encoding. Elaboration is a deeper form of encoding.

The graph on the next page shows a typical set of results for this experiment.

contd

Items at the beginning of the sequence are remembered well because there has been time for rehearsal and transfer to the long-term memory. Items at the end of the sequence have not been displaced from the short-term memory and are, therefore, also recalled well. However, items in the middle of the sequence are poorly recalled as they have been displaced from the short-term memory.

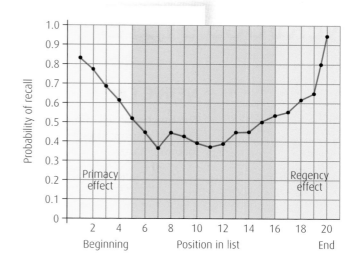

Long-Term Memory (LTM)

Transfer of information into the long-term memory can be made more successful by **elaborating meaning**. This works by devising a little story about the item to be remembered – making the information stand out.

Retrieving information from long-term memory is made easier if you are in the same setting or context as you were when the information was encoded. Here, particular sights, sounds, smells or emotions act as **contextual cues**, triggering retrieval of a memory. For example, visiting your old home or school can evoke memories of your childhood, or the smell of a perfume as you enter a room can evoke memories of a particular person or an event.

Location of Memory in the Brain

Parts of the brain associated with storage of memories include areas of the cerebral cortex.

The site of long-term memory storage depends on the type of memory.

 THINGS TO DO AND THINK ABOUT

Short-Term Memory Span
You should be familiar with the method used to determine the capacity of the short-term memory.
1   Subjects are asked to put pens and pencils down before starting the experiment (to prevent cheating).
2   A series of three letters or numbers is read out one at a time, in a monotone voice and at regular speed.
3   Subjects pick up pens and pencils, and write down the series.
4   The procedure is repeated with the number of items in the series increasing each time.
5   A second set of numbers is then used to increase reliability.
6   The maximum number of items that can be recalled correctly by each subject is taken as their memory span, with class results being pooled to determine the maximum and minimum memory span for the class.

A typical set of results would show the memory span to range from 5 to 9 items, i.e. 7 ± 2.

 DON'T FORGET

Contextual cues are built up during encoding; elaboration adds to the number of contextual cues for each piece of information. The more contextual cues that are present, the easier the recall.

 DON'T FORGET

Transfer from STM to LTM is by rehearsal, organisation and elaboration.

ONLINE

Learn more about memory by following the links at www.brightredbooks.net

 ONLINE TEST

Test your knowledge of memory at www. brightredbooks.net

NERVOUS SYSTEM

NERVE CELLS

The functional cell of the nervous system is the nerve cell or **neuron**. There are three types of neuron: **sensory**, **motor** and **inter neuron**. Each neuron consists of the following parts:

> **Dendrite** Dendrites receive nerve impulses and send them towards the cell body.

> **Cell body** The cell body contains the nucleus.

> **Axon** The axon carries the nerve impulse away from the cell body.

Sensory Neurons

DON'T FORGET

The cell body of a sensory neuron sticks up from the rest of the nerve like a little lollipop.

Sensory neurons pass information from **sense organs** to neurons in the central nervous system (CNS). A single dendrite receives information from sense receptors and transmits a nerve impulse towards the cell body. From the cell body, a single axon carries the nerve impulse into the spinal cord where the impulse is transmitted to the dendrites of an **inter neuron**.

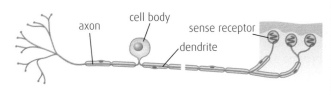

Inter Neurons

Inter neurons lie completely within the CNS. They vary in shape but, in general, have several dendrites and an axon extending from the cell body, allowing messages to be passed on to a large number of neurons.

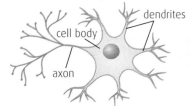

Motor Neurons

DON'T FORGET

Receptors on the post-synaptic membrane determine whether the signal is excitatory or inhibitory.

Motor neurons transmit nerve impulses from the CNS to an effector organ (muscle or gland). The cell body and several short dendrites lie embedded in the CNS. One axon extends from the cell body, passing out of the CNS to reach the effector organ.

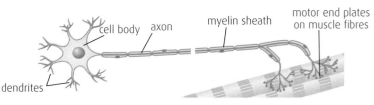

THE SYNAPSE

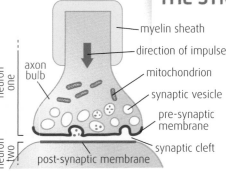

A synapse is the junction between an axon of one cell and a dendrite of another, and allows the transmission of nerve impulses between neurons.

The nerve impulse passes down the axon to reach the **axon bulb**, where it stimulates **synaptic vesicles** to move towards and fuse with the **pre-synaptic membrane**, releasing neurotransmitter chemicals by exocytosis. Neurotransmitters diffuse across the **synaptic cleft** to reach the **post-synaptic membrane**, where they fuse with receptors. If a large enough number of receptors are activated, the post-synaptic membrane reaches its **threshold** and the nerve impulse is transmitted onwards.

Neurotransmitters must be rapidly removed from the post-synaptic membrane. Otherwise, it would be impossible to control the frequency of nerve impulses, and you would not be able to distinguish between stronger and weaker stimuli (such as bright and dim light).

contd

Neurotransmitter Substances

You should be familiar with two neurotransmitter substances:

Acetylcholine is removed by enzymatic degradation. The enzyme acetylcholinesterase breaks down the neurotransmitter and the inactive products are reabsorbed by the pre-synaptic cell. They are recycled and used to make more acetylcholine.

Noradrenaline leaves the post-synaptic membrane and is reabsorbed intact by the pre-synaptic cell. Within the pre-synaptic cell, noradrenaline is enclosed within vesicles for reuse.

DON'T FORGET

If not enough neurotransmitter is released to reach the threshold, the nerve impulse will not be transmitted. However, a series of weak stimuli can together allow that threshold to be reached in a process called **stimulation**.

MYELINATION

The speed of conduction of a nerve impulse is increased by the neuron's **myelin sheath**. **Myelin** is formed by **glial cells** which wrap themselves round and round axons, building up layers of cell membrane. Some diseases destroy the myelin sheath, causing loss of muscle co-ordination.

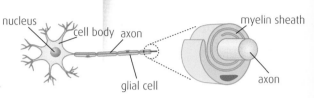

Myelination is incomplete at birth but continues to adolescence, being completed in the upper limbs before the lower limbs. As a result, babies cannot coordinate their movements at birth and gain control of their arms before their legs. During the first two years of life, an infant's responses to stimuli are not as rapid or co-ordinated as those of an older child.

NEURAL PATHWAYS

The route that a nerve impulse follows through the nervous system is called a **neural pathway**. New neural pathways are formed to allow new responses to stimuli, suppress reflexes or to bypass tissue damage. This ability to remodel is called **plasticity**. You should be familiar with three types of neural pathway: converging, diverging and reverberating neural pathways.

ONLINE

Follow the link to the animation of the synapse at www.brightredbooks.net to learn more.

Converging Neural Pathways

In a **converging neural pathway**, impulses from different sources are directed to one neuron. This increases the sensitivity to excitatory or inhibitory signals, and allows weak stimuli to be amplified, as in the visual pathway. Within the retina, the rods that detect low light release only a small amount of neurotransmitter into the synaptic gap. However, a cumulative effect results through the synapse of several rods with the same post-synaptic neuron, bringing about the transmission of a nerve impulse (**summation**).

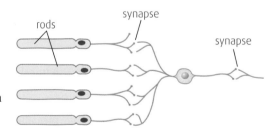

Diverging Neural Pathways

In a diverging pathway, a single pre-synaptic neuron forms synapses with several post-synaptic neurons, allowing the pathway to reach several destinations at the same time.

Diverging neural pathways allow fine motor control, where several skeletal muscles work together to produce precise movements, such as in the fingers or eyes.

Reverberating Neural Pathways

In a reverberating pathway, neurons link back to form synapses with neurons earlier in the chain, so that the nerve impulse passes repeatedly through the circuit. An example is the neural pathway that controls breathing.

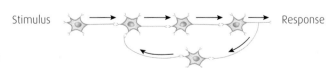

ONLINE TEST

Take the test on the nervous system online at www.brightredbooks.net

 THINGS TO DO AND THINK ABOUT

Glial cells do more than produce the myelin sheath. Describe the other roles that they perform.

NEUROTRANSMITTERS AND RECREATIONAL DRUGS

Neurotransmitters are chemicals that transmit nerve impulses across synapses from one neuron to the next (see previous page). Some neurotransmitters are involved in controlling mood. These include:

- **endorphins** – involved in pain relief and give a feeling of euphoria (similar to the effect of **opiates**)
- **dopamine** – involved with feeling pleasure.

ENDORPHINS

There are about 20 different **endorphins**. They function by attaching to receptors on neurons, **blocking the transmission of pain signals**. The increased production of endorphins in response to very severe pain enables continued body function while the individual finds help, increasing the chances of survival. Endorphins also have a role in the regulation of appetite and cause the release of sex hormones.

Endorphins are produced under other circumstances:

- During extended periods of physical exercise, endorphin production increases, producing feelings of euphoria. Their action inhibits the production of an inhibitory neurotransmitter, unblocking the **reward pathway**. Dopamine is produced as a result of increased endorphins in the reward pathway.
- physical and emotional stress
- during eating of some foods, such as dark chocolate.

DOPAMINE

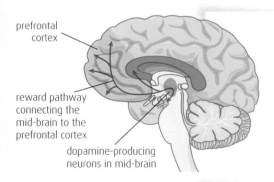

prefrontal cortex

reward pathway connecting the mid-brain to the prefrontal cortex

dopamine-producing neurons in mid-brain

When humans participate in activities that are beneficial to them (involving natural rewards such as food or artificial ones such as drugs), the pleasurable feelings act as positive reinforcement, making it more likely that the behaviour will be repeated. The **reward pathway** which produces these feelings of pleasure connects dopamine-producing neurons in the **mid-brain** with neurons in the **prefrontal areas** and **base of the cerebral cortex**. Dopamine also has a role in controlling motor function through a separate pathway.

TREATMENT OF NEUROTRANSMITTER DISORDERS

When there is either an overproduction or underproduction of neurotransmitter, or if there is an imbalance in neurotransmitter production, a neurotransmitter disorder can result. These include:

- Alzheimer's disease
- Parkinson's disease
- schizophrenia
- anxiety disorders
- depression.

To treat these disorders, drugs that are similar to neurotransmitters are prescribed. These act as **agonists**, **antagonists** and **enzyme inhibitors**.

Agonists

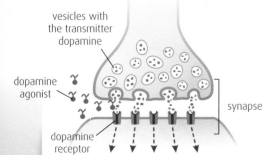

vesicles with the transmitter dopamine

dopamine agonist

dopamine receptor

synapse

the message is passed on

Agonists are drugs that mimic the function of a neurotransmitter. They bind to the same receptor as the neurotransmitter, bringing about a normal response. Dopamine agonists are used in the treatment of Parkinson's disease.

contd

Antagonists

Antagonists are drugs that prevent the neurotransmitter binding to its receptor on the post-synaptic membrane, by competing with the neurotransmitter for the receptor-binding site or by causing a change in shape of the receptor, so that the neurotransmitter cannot bind. Dopamine antagonists are used to block dopamine receptors when treating schizophrenia, which is caused – in part – by the overstimulation of dopamine receptors in the reward pathway.

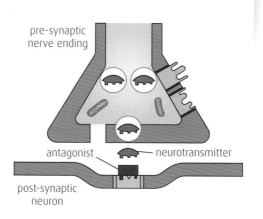

pre-synaptic nerve ending

antagonist — neurotransmitter

post-synaptic neuron

Enzyme Inhibitors

Neurotransmitters are normally removed from the post-synaptic membrane by enzyme action or by re-uptake into the pre-synaptic neuron. Enzyme inhibitors work by preventing this. For example, in the treatment of Alzheimer's disease, an enzyme inhibitor slows down acetylcholinesterase, the enzyme which breaks down acetylcholine, maintaining its concentration.

RECREATIONAL DRUGS AND ADDICTION

Recreational drugs often mimic the action of neurotransmitters in the reward pathway, altering brain neurochemistry and changing mood, cognition, perception and behaviour. The heightened release of dopamine in the reward pathway provides the motivation to repeat the act, often leading to addiction. As with drugs used to treat neurotransmitter disorders, recreational drugs can act as:

- agonists – ethanol binds to receptors on the post-synaptic membrane causing widespread changes to behaviour; nicotine is a dopamine agonist, binding to dopamine receptors to produce feelings of a 'dopamine high'

- antagonists – ethanol blocks the glutamate receptor NMDA, which is involved in memory

- inhibitors – cocaine blocks the mechanism which removes excess dopamine and serotonin from the synapse by binding to the molecules that transport them across the synaptic cleft. They cannot, therefore, be reabsorbed into the pre-synaptic neurons.

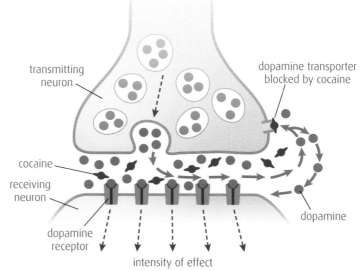

transmitting neuron

dopamine transporter blocked by cocaine

cocaine

receiving neuron

dopamine

dopamine receptor

intensity of effect

Addiction

When drugs that act as **antagonists** are abused over time, the body reacts to the reduced stimulation of receptors by increasing the number of receptors and their sensitivity to the drug. This is called **sensitisation** and leads to **addiction**, where the individual craves more of the drug.

Long-term use of drugs that act as **agonists** causes a decrease in the number and sensitivity of receptors for the drug (**desensitisation**). Larger and larger doses of the drug are needed for an equivalent effect (**drug tolerance**).

 THINGS TO DO AND THINK ABOUT

Research online the mode of action of the recreational drug Ecstasy.

IMMUNOLOGY

Humans often live in dense populations and, so, are at risk from transmitted diseases. **Immunology** is the study of the *immune system*, both when healthy and during disease. The **immune system** is a complex system of biological structures and *processes* which detect and destroy a wide variety of pathogens (bacteria and viruses and other disease-causing organisms) and so protects against *disease*. The human body can also protect itself against some toxins and cancer cells via the immune system. **Immunity** is the ability of the body to resist infection by a pathogen, or to destroy it if it invades the body.

DON'T FORGET

The physical barriers and their secretions are the human body's first line of defence.

DON'T FORGET

The trachea and bronchi of the respiratory tract are lined with cilia which beat rhythmically to move mucus containing trapped microbes upwards to the mouth, where it can be swallowed.

DON'T FORGET

The increased blood flow that occurs as part of the inflammatory response results in heat and redness of the damaged tissue.

NON-SPECIFIC BODY DEFENCES

Physical and Chemical Defences

The body has natural barriers to prevent entry by pathogens. Closely packed **epithelial cells** form the outer covering of skin and are found in the inner linings of the digestive system and respiratory system. They form a physical barrier and have specialised cells which produce **secretions** such as mucus, wax or oil. These chemical secretions trap dirt and prevent invasion by pathogens. Various glands in the skin and the tear glands produce chemical secretions with antimicrobial properties. Tears, saliva and sweat contain a powerful enzyme, lysozyme, which breaks down the cell walls of airborne pathogens. The mucus secreted by the epithelial cells of the respiratory tract and the upper gastrointestinal tract is sticky and so traps foreign particles, which are then swept upwards (as in the respiratory tract) or destroyed by **phagocytes**. Hairs in the nose trap foreign particles, and the cough and sneeze reflexes remove foreign bodies from the throat and nose. Stomach acid destroys many pathogens that are taken in with food.

First lines of defence

saliva
antibacterial
enzymes

skin
prevents
entry

stomach acid
low pH kills
harmful
microbes

tears
antibacterial
enzymes

mucus
linings
trap
dirt and
microbes

'good' gut
bacteria
out compete
bad

Inflammatory Response

The inflammatory response is the body's reaction to injury or infection by pathogens and is localised to the site of injury or infection. Special white blood cells, called **mast cells**, which are present in the connective tissues of the body and in organs, play a key role. If tissue damage occurs, mast cells are activated and release the chemical **histamine**. Histamine increases the permeability of capillaries and causes blood vessels to dilate **(vasodilation)**, increasing blood flow to the site of infection.

The increase in the flow of blood to the damaged tissue caused by white blood cells in the damaged area, results in an increase in the number of phagocytes and clotting elements at the site of infection.

The increase in blood-clotting chemicals promotes the coagulation of blood at the damaged tissue, halting blood loss and preventing further infection.

contd

Phagocytes and Phagocytosis

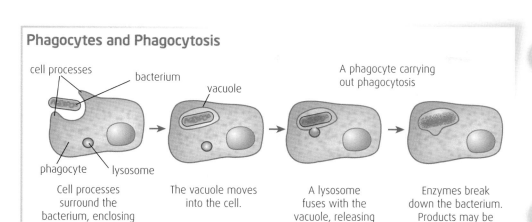

cell processes

bacterium

vacuole

A phagocyte carrying out phagocytosis

phagocyte   lysosome

Cell processes surround the bacterium, enclosing it in a vacuole.

The vacuole moves into the cell.

A lysosome fuses with the vacuole, releasing digestive enzymes.

Enzymes break down the bacterium. Products may be reused by the cell.

- The phagocytes recognise pathogens.
- The phagocytes engulf the pathogens.
- The phagocytes destroy the pathogens by phagocytosis using digestive enzymes within the lysosomes.
- The increase in blood-clotting chemicals promotes the coagulation of blood at the damaged tissue, halting blood loss and preventing further infection.
- Phagocytes release cytokines (protein molecules which act as a signal to specific white blood cells).
- Cytokines attract more phagocytes to the site of infection.

The inflammatory response

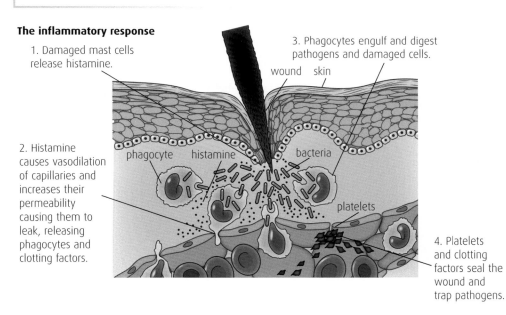

1. Damaged mast cells release histamine.

3. Phagocytes engulf and digest pathogens and damaged cells.

wound   skin

2. Histamine causes vasodilation of capillaries and increases their permeability causing them to leak, releasing phagocytes and clotting factors.

phagocyte   histamine

bacteria

platelets

4. Platelets and clotting factors seal the wound and trap pathogens.

THINGS TO DO AND THINK ABOUT

1 Describe two ways in which epithelial cells provide defence against pathogens.

2 Explain the role of the following in the inflammatory response:
   a mast cells   b histamine   c phagocytes   d platelets.

3 Draw a diagram showing how phagocytes engulf and destroy pathogens.

4 Describe the role of cytokines in phagocytosis.

VIDEO LINK

Watch the video clip at www.brightredbooks.net which describes the inflammatory response.

ONLINE TEST

Test yourself on your knowledge of immunology online at www.brightredbooks.net

DON'T FORGET

The inflammatory response and the actions of phagocytes are the body's second line of defence.

 ONLINE

Find out more about the inflammatory response at www.brightredbooks.net

SPECIFIC CELLULAR DEFENCES AGAINST PATHOGENS 1

As well as non-specific defence mechanisms against disease, humans have an additional and sophisticated mechanism which is capable of recognising and destroying **specific** substances.

DON'T FORGET

A clone is a group of cells or organisms that are genetically identical.

DON'T FORGET

An antigen is a protein that is found on the surface of a pathogen and which is unique to that particular pathogen. An antigen is recognised by the body as non-self (foreign).

LYMPHOCYTES

Lymphocytes are a group of white blood cells involved in the specific immune response. Antigens are molecules, often proteins, which are located on the surface of cells e.g. on the surface of pathogens, which trigger this response. Each lymphocyte has a single type of membrane receptor which is specific for one antigen. The body has a huge number of different lymphocytes, each with a different membrane receptor. Therefore, different lymphocytes respond to different specific antigens on invading pathogens. Antigen binding leads to repeated lymphocyte division resulting in the formation of a clonal population of identical lymphocytes.

Stages in Clonal Selection

Stage 1: An antigen binds to its specific receptor on a lymphocyte.

Stage 2: The specific lymphocyte undergoes repeated division, resulting in the formation of a clone of identical lymphocytes.

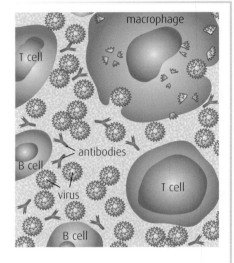

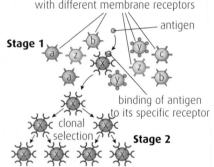

a, b, c, y and z are different lymphocytes with different membrane receptors

The clonal selection theory of antibody production

DON'T FORGET

Lymphocytes respond to antigens on foreign cells, cells infected by pathogens and toxins released by pathogens.

CELL-MEDIATED IMMUNITY

There are two types of lymphocytes: B lymphocytes and T lymphocytes.

B Lymphocytes

B lymphocytes are produced and mature in the bone marrow. B lymphocytes produce **antibodies** against antigens, which leads to the destruction of the pathogen. Antibodies are Y-shaped molecules with receptor-binding sites (see diagram). These binding sites are specific to a particular antigen on a particular pathogen. An antibody matches an antigen much like a key matches a lock. The antibody binds to the antigen to form an antigen–antibody complex that inactivates the pathogen or toxin and which can then be destroyed by phagocytosis.

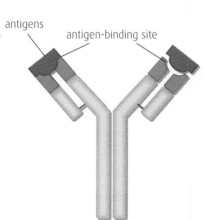

An antibody is a y-shaped protein. Each tip of the y has an antigen-binding site specific to a particular antigen.

Example:

One type of B cell makes antibodies against the virus that causes the common cold, while a different type produces antibodies that attack bacteria which cause pneumonia.

ALLERGY

Sometimes the body over reacts to a small trace of a harmless foreign substance and the person suffers an **allergic response**. This happens because B lymphocytes respond to antigens on substances which are harmless to the body. The antigen involved is called an **allergen**. Typical allergens include animal hair, pollen, moulds and dust mites. An allergic reaction involves the production of histamine, resulting in inflammation and damage to tissues.

Some common diseases caused by allergic reactions are hay fever, anaphylactic shock and allergic asthma.

Hay fever

Anaphylactic shock

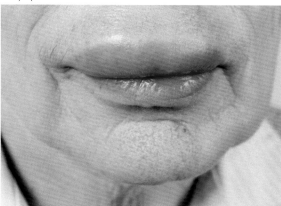

Allergic asthma

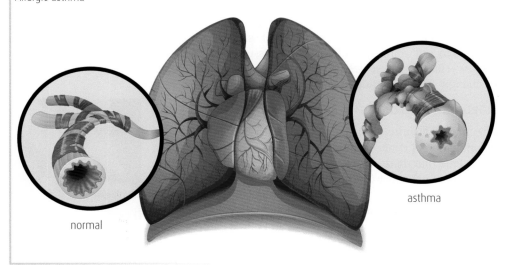

normal

asthma

VIDEO LINK

Watch the video clip about fighting infection by clonal selection at www.brightredbooks.net

DON'T FORGET

The immune response is specific and is the body's third line of defence.

ONLINE

Read about the causes and symptoms of hay fever at www.brightredbooks.net

ONLINE

Read about the causes and symptoms of anaphylactic shock at www.brightredbooks.net

ONLINE

Read about the causes and symptoms of allergic asthma at www.brightredbooks.net

VIDEO LINK

Watch the video about the allergic reaction at www.brightredbooks.net

THINGS TO DO AND THINK ABOUT

1 Write a few sentences to explain the clonal selection theory of antibody production.

2 Draw a diagram and label it to show:
   a an antibody
   b the antigen-binding sites
   c the antigen–antibody complex.

3 a Describe what is meant by an allergic response.
   b What is the cause of this type of reaction?

ONLINE TEST

Take the test on specific cellular defence at www.brightredbooks.net

SPECIFIC CELLULAR DEFENCES AGAINST PATHOGENS 2

T LYMPHOCYTES

T lymphocytes are produced in the bone marrow and then migrate through the bloodstream to the thymus gland in the upper chest area of the body, where they mature. T lymphocytes can be distinguished from other lymphocytes by their cell-surface receptors which allow them to detect specific foreign substances (antigens) that enter the body. There is a direct interaction between the T lymphocytes and invading pathogen. T lymphocytes destroy infected body cells by recognising the pathogen's antigens on the cell membrane and inducing **apoptosis**. Apoptosis is programmed cell death.

Apoptosis

- T lymphocytes attach to infected cells and release proteins.

- Proteins diffuse into infected cells.

- This causes the production of self-destructive enzymes.

- These enzymes cause cell death.

- Remains of cell are removed by phagocytosis.

These specific surface proteins normally allow the T lymphocytes to distinguish between self-antigens on body's own cells and non-self-antigens on infected or foreign cells.

CASE STUDIES

AUTOIMMUNE DISEASE

An autoimmune disease occurs when the regulation of the immune system fails and it can no longer distinguish between healthy tissue and antigens. T lymphocytes start to respond to 'self'-antigens and, so, healthy tissue is attacked, resulting in an autoimmune disease. This may cause destruction of healthy body tissue, abnormal growth of an organ or changes in the function of an organ.

Rheumatoid Arthritis

Rheumatoid arthritis is an autoimmune disease that causes inflammation of joints, resulting in pain and swelling. It has been discovered that there are a large number of cytokines active in the joints of patients with rheumatoid arthritis and that these chemicals promote the disease. A loss of regulation, leading to an imbalance between pro- and anti-inflammatory cytokines, results in inflammation and the destruction of the joint.

Type 1 Diabetes

Type 1 diabetes occurs when the body does not produce enough insulin, a hormone which controls the glucose content of the blood. It is an autoimmune disease in which the immune system attacks and destroys the insulin-producing cells (beta cells) in the pancreas.

Multiple Sclerosis

Multiple sclerosis is an autoimmune disease which damages the myelin sheath, the protective fatty covering of nerve cells. The nerve damage is caused by inflammation whereby the body's own immune cells (T cells) attack antigens on the myelin sheath, resulting in its damage and so nerve impulses slow down or stop. This damage can occur in any area of the central nervous system including the brain, optic nerve and spinal cord.

DON'T FORGET

The clonal selection theory explains how the body can produce such a wide range of different antibodies.

ONLINE

Read more about the immune response at www.brightredbooks.net

ONLINE

Read more about rheumatoid arthritis at www.brightredbooks.net

VIDEO LINK

Watch the video about type 1 diabetes at www.brightredbooks.net

ONLINE

Read more about multiple sclerosis at www.brightredbooks.net

IMMUNOLOGICAL MEMORY

Some of the cloned T and B lymphocytes produced in response to antigens by **clonal selection** survive long term as **memory cells**. Immunological memory is the ability of the immune system to respond more quickly and more effectively to a subsequent infection by the same antigen. When a secondary exposure to the same antigen occurs these memory cells quickly bring about the production of a new clone of specific lymphocytes. These destroy the invading pathogens before the individual shows any symptoms of the disease. During this secondary immunological response, the production of antibodies is greater and more rapid than in the primary response. Immunological memory is specific for a particular antigen and is long-lived.

Memory B cells exist long after the infection has subsided and, so, are available to stimulate the appropriate immune response.

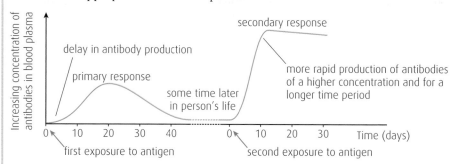

VIDEO LINK

Watch the video which describes the roles of different T cells at www.brightredbooks.net

ONLINE

Read about the action of T and B lymphocytes at www.brightredbooks.net

DIRECT ATTACK ON THE IMMUNE SYSTEM

A direct attack on the immune system, which removes a function or causes part of it to fail, will increase the likelihood of infection.

HIV

HIV (human immunodeficiency virus) directly attacks the immune system, by attacking and destroying T lymphocytes. The resulting depletion of T lymphocytes increases susceptibility to infection and leads to the development of AIDS (acquired immune deficiency syndrome). This means the immune system is weakened and therefore the body is more vulnerable and susceptible to infections, which can be life threatening.

VIDEO LINK

Find out about HIV infection at www.brightredbooks.net

Tuberculosis

Tuberculosis (TB) is a highly infectious bacterial disease which affects the lungs. The bacterium can persist in some people, since it can survive *within* phagocytes and so avoids detection by the immune system.

 THINGS TO DO AND THINK ABOUT

1 Describe what causes an autoimmune disease.

2 a Using the graph shown above, describe differences between the primary and secondary responses to infection by a particular antigen.
   b Explain why the secondary response differs from the primary response.

3 Research and write about public health measures and drug therapies used in the control of HIV.

ONLINE TEST

Take the test on specific cellular defence at www.brightredbooks.net

IMMUNISATION 1

Immunisation is a process whereby a person develops protection from (immunity to) a particular pathogenic micro-organism and subsequently the infection associated with that micro-organism. Immunity can be developed by **vaccination**.

DON'T FORGET

An infectious disease is caused by a pathogen and can be spread from one person to another.

DON'T FORGET

An adjuvant is a pharmacological agent which is added to a drug to increase or aid its effect.

DON'T FORGET

The aim of any vaccination programme is to reduce or eliminate a particular disease.

VACCINATION

People can be made resistant to a particular disease by **vaccination**. This is when a **vaccine** (containing antigenic material from an infectious pathogen) is administered, which stimulates a person's immune system to produce antibodies against the antigen. Memory cells are also created, thus developing immunological memory. The infectious pathogens can be inactivated pathogen toxins, dead pathogens, parts of pathogens or weakened pathogens.

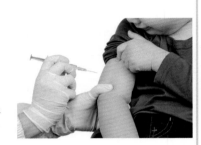

When producing the vaccine, the antigens from the infectious pathogen are usually mixed with an **adjuvant**. This is a substance which makes the vaccine more effective and so enhances the immune response. Types of antigen which are used in vaccination are shown in the table.

Type of antigen used in a vaccine	Examples of diseases for which this type of antigen is used as a vaccine
Inactivated pathogen toxins	Tetanus, diphtheria
Dead pathogens	Polio, hepatitis A
Parts of pathogens	HPV, hepatitis B
Weakened pathogens	Measles, mumps, rubella

HERD IMMUNITY

Herd immunity occurs when a **significant proportion** of a population is immunised against a particular infection. Establishing herd immunity is important in reducing the spread of infection. Those individuals who have not been vaccinated and who are non-immune are protected since there will be a lower probability of them coming into contact with infected people.

 immunised and healthy

 not immunised but still healthy

not immunised, sick and contagious

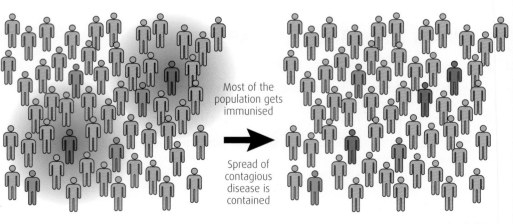

Most of the population gets immunised

Spread of contagious disease is contained

contd

The Importance of Herd Immunity

Herd immunity is important in reducing the spread of diseases in a community, but can also be crucial for protecting vulnerable groups of people who cannot be vaccinated, for example:

- people with a weakened immune system, such as those undergoing chemotherapy
- new-born babies and children who are too young to be vaccinated
- elderly people
- HIV-infected people
- people who are seriously ill.

Herd Immunity Threshold

The **herd immunity threshold** is the proportion of individuals in a population who must be immune to prevent a particular disease spreading. Instead the disease will decrease to a low baseline level. This threshold depends on several factors.

Factor affecting herd immunity threshold	Explanation
Type of disease	The proportion of the population that must be immunised in order to achieve herd immunity is different for different diseases. More virulent diseases require a greater percentage of vaccination in the population to give the desired herd immunity.
The efficacy of the vaccine used in immunisation	The effectiveness of the vaccine affects the threshold. This can be determined using a clinical trial.
Density of population	The number of contacts made with other individuals in a population in a certain period of time affects the threshold. This will depend on the population density.

If immunisation rates fall, herd immunity can break down, resulting in an increase in new cases of infection. Herd immunity eradicated smallpox and explains why diseases such as polio and diphtheria are rare in developed nations where there are well-established vaccination programmes.

 DON'T FORGET

The herd immunity threshold is the proportion of individuals who must be immune so that a particular disease will no longer spread through the population, but decrease to low incidence.

 **ONLINE**

Head over to www.brightredbooks.net for useful links, videos, tests and more!

MASS VACCINATION

Mass vaccination is the immunisation of a large number of people in a particular location at one time or within a short time interval. The aim of a mass vaccination programme is to establish herd immunity to a disease. Sometimes difficulties can arise with a planned mass vaccination programme and so herd immunity is difficult to establish in some populations.

- In developing countries widespread vaccination may not be possible due to malnutrition and poverty. Poverty prevents access to health services since vaccination may not be affordable for all.

- In developed countries, vaccinations may be rejected by a percentage of the population. Some parents choose not to have their children immunised due to fears over the safety or possible side effects of vaccines.

DON'T FORGET

Antibodies are produced by B lymphocytes. Specific antibodies recognise and combine with specific antigens.

 THINGS TO DO AND THINK ABOUT

1. Describe how vaccination can make someone immune to a disease.

2. Explain why a vaccine normally contains an adjuvant.

3. Research and write a paragraph about the success of mass vaccination programmes for (i) tuberculosis, (ii) polio and (iii) smallpox.

4. Explain why herd immunity may not be successfully established in (i) a developing country and (ii) a developed country.

5. Explain what is meant by herd immunity and why this can be established even although only 90% of the population is immunised.

IMMUNISATION 2

Immunisation programmes are run in Scotland with children and adults receiving vaccines at appropriate times and stages in their lives.

EXAMPLES

The population of Scotland is protected through immunisation against a number of infectious diseases. As shown in the table, each of these diseases has a different herd immunity threshold.

Diseases for which vaccination is routine in Scotland	Herd immunity threshold, % (where available)
Diphtheria	85
Whooping cough	92–94
Polio	80–86
Measles, mumps and rubella (MMR)	Measles 83–94 Mumps 75–86 Rubella 83–85
Tetanus	N/A *
Haemophilus influenzae type b (Hib)	Data unavailable
Meningococcal C disease (Men C)	Data unavailable
Pneumococcal infection	Data unavailable
Human Papilloma Virus (HPV)	Data unavailable

*Herd immunity only applies to diseases that are contagious. It does not apply to diseases such as tetanus where the vaccine protects **only** the vaccinated person.

ANTIGENIC VARIATION

The human immune system has developed specific mechanisms to defend the body against pathogens. However, pathogens have also developed various strategies, through the process of evolution, to evade the immune system. This has consequences for vaccination strategies.

Some pathogens avoid the effect of immunological memory by changing their surface proteins (antigens). This is **antigenic variation**. Mutations in the pathogen's DNA give rise to these changes. Antibodies in the body no longer recognise the pathogen since memory cells produced from an initial infection fail to recognise the new antigens and so the memory cells are no longer effective against the pathogen. A current vaccine will not protect against a new form of the disease, so antigenic variation also makes it difficult to develop new vaccines for certain infections.

The Role and Impact of Antigenic Variation in Influenza

Antigenic variation occurs in the influenza (flu) virus. Therefore, the memory cells produced due to an infection by one strain of the flu virus will not recognise the antigens of a new strain. This explains why flu is still a major public health problem and why those at risk from complications from influenza must be vaccinated annually.

Bioinformatics software can be used to study the differences in DNA or protein sequences between different strains of influenza viruses.

There are two different ways in which the influenza virus can change over time:

1 Antigenic drift is a small change in the flu virus that happens slowly over a long period of time. Mutations in the genes of the virus occur as the virus replicates and over time a virus with different antigenic properties evolves.

2 Antigenic shift happens when two or more different strains of the flu virus infect the same cell and their genomes combine. This can happen suddenly and results in a major change to the virus.

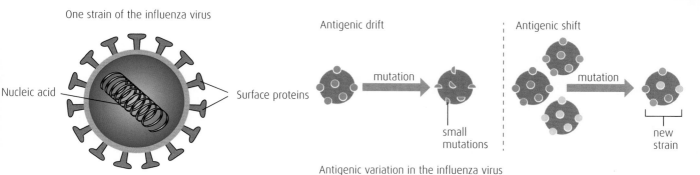

Antigenic variation in the influenza virus

THINGS TO DO AND THINK ABOUT

1 Explain how some pathogens can evade the specific immune response by antigenic variation.

2 Why must the influenza vaccine be administered annually?

3 Explain what is meant by antigenic variation.

4 A different vaccine is needed for each strain of the influenza virus. Why are different vaccines required?

CLINICAL TRIALS OF VACCINES AND DRUGS

All new pharmaceutical products (including vaccines) must undergo **clinical trials** before being licensed for use. After a vaccine has been developed and tested in a lab, clinical trials (in humans) are needed to establish **safety**, determine **effectiveness** as a treatment and to discover any **side effects**.

DESIGN OF CLINICAL TRIALS

As in all scientific investigations, a vaccine clinical trial must use procedures that ensure a fair and valid trial, including:

1 Randomisation

In a **randomised** clinical trial, there is an experimental group of people who are given the new treatment and a control group who are given no treatment or a placebo. Participants are assigned randomly to each group to reduce bias in the distribution of characteristics (e.g. age and gender).

Randomised controlled trials

patients — random assignment — treatment group / control group — follow-up / follow-up — compare results

Key

- ■ no disease
- ■ contracted disease

> **DON'T FORGET** ✚
>
> A placebo is an inactive drug or treatment which is used in a clinical trial.

> **ONLINE** ➡
>
> Find out about the design of clinical trials and their use in the development of vaccines at www.brightredbooks.net

2 Double-blind

In a **double-blind** study neither the investigator nor the participant is aware of the nature of the treatment the subject is receiving, so expectations of the researcher and the subject do not affect the outcome. One group of subjects would receive the vaccine or drug while the second group would receive a placebo control. This would prevent a biased interpretation of the results and ensure valid comparisons.

3 Placebo

To assess a vaccine or drug, it must be compared to an alternative treatment, for example a previously licensed vaccine or an inactive substance. A **placebo** is a 'dummy' treatment with no active ingredient.

4 Sample Size

The **sample size** (the number of participants assigned to the control and the experimental groups) affects the reliability of the results of a clinical trial. The larger the group size, the smaller the magnitude of experimental error and the greater the statistical significance of the results.

5 Analysis of Results

Once a study is completed, the results from the experimental group and the control group are compared to determine if there is a **statistically significant difference** between treatment and control groups.

 THINGS TO DO AND THINK ABOUT

1 Explain why any new drug or vaccine must undergo clinical trials.

2 Explain how a clinical trial ensures randomisation.

3 What is a placebo?

4 How is a clinical trial designed to maximise reliability?

5 Explain how error bars can be used to show if there is a significant difference between the experimental and the control group when the results of a clinical trial are made available.

6 Research the results of some clinical trials. Try to find graphs of the results which show error bars and explain whether or not the results are statistically significant.

7 Describe how a clinical trial is designed to ensure the results are fair and valid.

 **DON'T FORGET**

In any scientific investigation, the larger the sample size, the more reliable are the results.

 **ONLINE TEST**

Test your knowledge of this topic on www.brightredbooks.net

REVISION QUESTIONS

QUESTION 1

The diagram below shows part of a neural pathway.

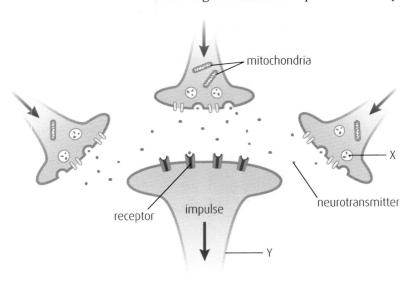

a   Name structure X.

b   Describe how neurotransmitter travels from structure X to bind to receptors on the post-synaptic membrane.

c   (i) Name one neurotransmitter, (ii) describe how it is removed from the post-synaptic membrane and (iii) explain why it must be removed from the post-synaptic membrane.

d   Which type of neural pathway is shown in the diagram?

e   This type of neural pathway can be found in the visual pathway. Explain how this type of pathway can assist in the transmission of impulses in dim light.

f   Identify the part of the neurone labelled Y.

g   A myelin sheath surrounds structure Y. Which type of cell produces the myelin sheath?

h   Some neurological conditions cause damage to the myelin sheath. What effect would this have on nerve function?

i   Some neurotransmitter disorders can be treated using drugs called antagonists. Describe how these drugs function.

j   Overuse of recreational drugs that act as antagonists results in addiction. Explain why.

QUESTION 2

The diagram shows the transfer of information into the long-term memory.

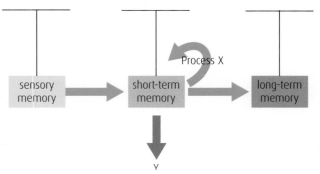

a   What term is used to describe the transformation of sensory information into a form that can be stored as a memory?

b   What happens to information that is not transferred to the long-term memory?

c   How many items can be stored in short-term memory?

d   Name process X.

e   Chunking can be used to improve short-term memory. Describe what is meant by 'chunking'.

f   Describe how contextual cues can assist with retrieval of information from long-term memory.

contd

QUESTION 3

a (i) Name the type of cells which form the outer covering of the skin and provides a physical barrier to the entry of pathogens.

   (ii) Describe another way in which these cells provide resistance to infection.

b During the inflammatory response, mast cells release a chemical. Name this chemical and describe its importance.

c Describe the role of (i) lysosomes and (ii) cytokines in the process of phagocytosis.

QUESTION 4

a Explain how a clonal population of lymphocytes forms following the invasion of the body by a pathogen.

b An allergy arises due to the failure of the immune system.

   (i) Which type of lymphocytes are involved in an allergic response?

   (ii) Describe how and why an allergy develops.

c Which of the following is a correct description of the cause of an autoimmune disease?

   A. B-lymphocytes respond to self-antigens.

   B. B-lymphocytes respond to foreign antigens.

   C. T-lymphocytes respond to self-antigens.

   D. T-lymphocytes respond to foreign antigens.

APPENDICES

ANSWERS

UNIT 1: HUMAN CELLS

Division and differentiation in human cells, pp.10–11

1   Vital and specialised genes

2   Pluripotent: able to form any type of specialised cell; multipotent: ability to form specialised cells is limited to those types found in the tissue from which they arise.

3   To provide a pool of stem cells for future needs.

Stem cells, pp.12–13

1   Testes and ovaries

2   a   More germline cells

    b   Gametes

3   Rapid, out-of-control cell division forms a tumour; a good blood supply forms to provide nutrients; the cells no longer stick to each other, so can be carried away by the blood circulation (metastasis).

4   Your answer should Include the following discussion points:

    Morality: responsibility to help patient versus the destruction of an embryo with the potential to live.

    Health: does the risk of developing tumours outweigh the chances of a cure?

    Safety: does the chance of a cure, using chemically altered cells, outweigh the chance of developing a different disease?

The structure of DNA, pp.14–15

1   16:9

2   a & b

    1 deoxyribose, 2 phosphate group, 3 cytosine, 4 adenine

    c   A: weak hydrogen; B strong chemical

3

Polymerase chain reaction (PCR), pp.16–17

1   Heating to 95°C separates the DNA strands, at 55°C primers can bind to the strands.

2   It would be denatured in the PCR process and amplification would not occur.

3.   A   3

     B   18 min

     C   24

     D   taq/thermo stable polymerase

     E   56 minutes

Gene expression, pp.18–19

1

	DNA	mRNA
Type of sugar	Deoxyribose	Ribose
Bases	Adenine, cytosine, guanine and thymine	Adenine, cytosine guanine and uracil
Number of strands	Two	One
Location	Only in nucleus	Moves from nucleus to cytoplasm

2   mRNA carries transcribed code from DNA to ribosome; tRNA anticodon matches with mRNA codon, bringing a specific amino acid into the correct position in a sequence; rRNA binds with proteins to form ribosomes which are the site of protein translation.

3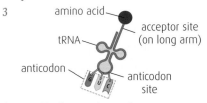

4   a   Nucleus and cytoplasm

    b   Cytoplasm

    c   Cytoplasm

Protein synthesis, pp.20–21

1   UCCGAUUGACGUUAGCUUUAC

2   Endonuclease, ligase, primer, free mRNA nucleotides, ATP, DNA template strand

3   1 DNA unwinds as RNA Polymerase moves along a section that codes for a protein. 2 The DNA strands separate when hydrogen bonds are broken. 3 Bases on the DNA strands are exposed. 4 mRNA nucleotides move in and form complementary base pairs with one of the DNA strands (the coding strand). Weak hydrogen bonds form. Cytosine always pairs with guanine; adenine on DNA pairs with uracil on mRNA, and thymine on DNA pairs with adenine on mRNA. 5 Strong chemical bonds form between the phosphate of one nucleotide and the ribose of the next nucleotide, building the mRNA strand. 6 The weak hydrogen bonds that were holding the DNA and mRNA strands together break, allowing the mRNA primary transcript to leave the nucleus and enter the cytoplasm. 7 Hydrogen bonds reform between the two DNA strands, and the DNA molecule rewinds to form a double helix.

4   Non-coding regions = introns, coding regions = exons

5   Primary transcript is longer as it contains introns.

One gene, many proteins, pp.22–23

1   a   Peptide   b   Hydrogen

    c   Primarily hydrogen with contributions from hydrophobic and ionic bonds.

2   Introns are spliced out but the same nucleotide sequence may be cut differently to produce different proteins.

Mutations, pp.24–25

1   a translocation   b duplication   c deletion

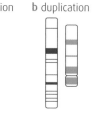

2   a   Substitution   b   Deletion   c   Insertion

Metabolism, pp.28–29

1   Pyruvate to lactic acid is a reversible reaction but pyruvate to ethanol + carbon dioxide is irreversible.

2   To save energy when the resultant protein is not required.

3   Different genes are expressed, resulting in different functions and appearance.

Enzyme action, pp.30–31

1   The active site of the enzyme is open and the substrate moves towards it. The active site closes bringing the substrate closer in and causing the reaction to occur. The resultant product triggers the opening of the active site and it is released.

2   Competitive: the inhibitor binds to the active site, preventing substrate from getting near. Non-competitive: the inhibitor binds to some other part of the enzyme, but changes the shape of the active site, thus preventing it binding with the substrate.

3   The shape of the active site is altered so no amount of substrate can react with it.

Cellular respiration, pp.32–33

1   Removes **hydrogen** ions and **electrons** from respiratory intermediates and passes them to the hydrogen carriers NAD (to form $NADH_2$) and FAD (to form $FADH_2$).

Exercise, pp.34–35

1   They have a richer blood supply.

2   Fast twitch 35: slow twitch 65

3

	Slow twitch	Fast twitch
Number of mitochondria	Many	Few
Blood supply	Rich	Poor
Source of energy	Fat	Glycogen, creatine phosphate
Type of activity	Endurance: cycling, long distance running	Short bursts: javelin, shot putt

Revision questions, pp.36–37

1

Statement	True/False	Correction
Somatic stem cells divide by mitosis to form somatic cells.	True	
Germline stem cells divide by mitosis and by meiosis.	True	
Division by <u>mitosis</u> produces haploid gametes.	False	meiosis

2   5,600

3   9

4   c); a); d); b).

5   a   Deletion.

b   It is a frame-shift mutation so will result in all triplet codes, and therefore the amino acids after translation being different after the mutated sequence.

6   (The rate of reaction has reached its maximum and is steady because all the active sites of the enzyme are occupied.

7   a   It removed hydrogen atoms and electrons.

b   It ensures that respiratory substrate is not wasted if not needed.

UNIT 2: PHYSIOLOGY AND HEALTH

Male reproductive system, pp.38–39

(i)   Testosterone level is unaffected because, like other hormones, it is transported in the blood.

(ii) Sperm production continues, but the sperm cannot pass into the urethra.

Cardiovascular system, pp.48–49

1   (a) Elastic fibres allow the artery to stretch as blood pulses through. (b) Smooth muscle in arteriole walls contracts to narrow the vessel.

2   Veins have valves to prevent backflow of blood.

3   Blood plasma contains proteins which are not present in tissue fluid.

The heart, pp.50–51

B

Pathology of cardiovascular disease (CVD) 1, pp.54–55

2   C

3   C

Pathology of cardiovascular disease (CVD) 2, pp.56–57

1   i   (c)   v   (g)   ix   (f)
    ii   (i)   vi   (b)   x   (d)
    iii (j)   vii (a)
    iv   (h)   viii (e)

2   B

3   D

4   D

ANSWERS (CONT)

Blood glucose level and diabetes, pp.58–59

1 Pancreas

2 X: insulin

   Y: glycogen

3 Liver

4 Glucose would be used up in respiration.

Obesity, pp.60–61

1 Between 1971 and 2000 there was an increase in the percentage of obese children in both boys and girls.

2 A

3 a Untrained male – 22.5
     Male athlete – 32.4
     Untrained female – 29.2
     Female athlete – 29.2

   b The trained female has a greater mass of muscle than the untrained female.

Revision questions, pp.62–63

1 a W: progesterone; X: oestrogen; Y: LH; Z: FSH.

   b Follicular cells in the ovary.

   Effects: (i) causes repair of the endometrium; (ii) causes surge in LH from the pituitary.

   c Ovulation.

   d Corpus luteum; secretes progesterone.

   e Inhibits release of FSH.

2 a 1. c; 2. d; 3. a; 4. b.

   b The oral contraceptive pill prevents the release of FSH and LH from the pituitary gland.

3 a X: X^HY; Y: X^hX^h; Z: X^HY.

   b (i) X^HX^h; (ii) carrier.

   c Haemophilia, red-green colour blindness, Duchenne muscular dystrophy

4 a Fluid A: tissue fluid; Fluid B: lymph; Vessel X: lymphatic capillary.

   b Pressure filtration.

   c Plasma proteins – too large to pass through wall of the blood capillary.

   d Valves.

   e Contraction of the surrounding muscles.

5 a Glycogen.

   b Pancreas.

   c (i) A decrease in the number of insulin receptors on cell membranes prevents glucose being converted into glycogen. (ii) After one hour some glucose is used by cells in respiration.

   d Glucagon.

UNIT 3: NEUROBIOLOGY AND IMMUNOLOGY

Nervous system, pp.68–69

Glial cells physically support the neurons and provide them with nutrition. They also remove debris by phagocytosis.

Immunology, pp.72–73

1 Epithelial cells form an outer layer that provides a physical barrier against the entry of pathogens. They also contain specialised cells which produce secretions that trap pathogens, e.g. wax, oil or mucus. Other glands produce antimicrobial chemicals.

2 a Mast cells release histamine in damaged tissues.

   b Histamine increases the permeability of capillaries and causes blood vessels to dilate, thus increasing blood flow to the site of infection.

   c Phagocytes engulf, digest and destroy pathogens by phagocytosis.

   d Platelets and other blood-clotting factors seal the wound and so trap pathogens.

3 See diagram on page 73.

4 Cytokines attract more phagocytes to the site of infection.

Specific cellular defences against pathogens 1, pp.74–75

1 The body has many different lymphocytes, each with different membrane receptors which are specific for one particular antigen. The clonal selection theory suggests that an antigen selects and binds to its receptor on the specific lymphocyte. The lymphocyte then undergoes repeated division, resulting in a clone of identical lymphocytes.

2

antigen-binding site   antigens   antigen-binding site

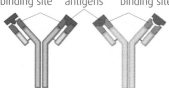

3 a An allergic response occurs when the body overreacts to a small trace of a harmless foreign substance.

   b Histamine is produced in response to the allergen, resulting in inflammation and damage to tissues.

Specific cellular defences against pathogens 2, pp.76–77

1 An autoimmune disease occurs when the immune system fails to distinguish between healthy cells and antigens. T Lymphocytes respond to self-antigens and, so, healthy tissues are attacked or function abnormally.

2 a The secondary response (i) produces antibodies more quickly, (ii) produces a higher concentration of antibodies and (iii) is longer lasting than the primary response (the antibodies remain in the blood for longer).

b These differences occur because of immunological memory. Some T and B lymphocytes which are produced in response to exposure to antigens survive as memory cells. Therefore, the immune system can respond more quickly and more effectively if exposed to the same antigen in the future.

3 Control of HIV infection

Public health measures	Drug therapies
Education about how virus is spread, promotion of safe sex, i.e. use of condoms, supplying drug addicts with clean needles.	There are several different antiretroviral drugs which stop HIV from replicating in the body at different stages of its life cycle.
	Other drugs are used to treat any associated infections.

Immunisation 1, pp.78–79

1 A vaccine containing antigenic material from an infectious pathogen is administered (e.g. by injection). This stimulates a person's immune system to produce antibodies against the antigen. Memory cells are also created, thus developing immunological memory. This means the immune system will respond more quickly and more effectively to a subsequent infection by the same antigen.

2 To make the vaccine more effective and enhance the immune response.

3 The effects of mass vaccination on:

(i) Tuberculosis (TB). Mass vaccination introduced in UK in 1950s has resulted in herd immunity and so now not everyone is vaccinated.

(ii) Polio. Mass vaccination has also resulted in herd immunity and polio is more or less absent from developed countries. Babies are routinely immunised at the age of 2 months.

(iii) Smallpox has been completely eradicated worldwide.

4 (i) Herd immunity may not be established in a developing country because widespread vaccination may not be possible due to poverty and/or malnutrition.

(ii) Herd immunity may not be established in a developed country because vaccinations may be rejected by some members of the population, due to fears over safety of the vaccine.

5 Herd immunity occurs when a significant proportion of a population is immunised against a particular infection, so reducing the spread of infection. Those individuals who have not been vaccinated and who are non-immune are protected since there will be a lower probability of them coming into contact with infected people

Immunisation 2, pp.80–81

1 They avoid the effect of immunological memory by changing their surface proteins (antigens).

2 Antigenic variation occurs in the influenza virus and so the memory cells produced due to an infection by one strain of the flu virus will not recognise the antigens of a new strain.

3 Antigenic variation occurs when certain pathogens evade the immune response by changing their surface antigens. Therefore, the antibodies present will not be able to recognise the altered antigens and so will not attack the pathogen.

4 Different vaccines are needed for each strain of the influenza virus because antigenic variation occurs in the influenza virus. The memory cells produced due to an infection by one strain of the virus will not recognise the antigens of the new strain.

Clinical trials of vaccines and drugs, pp.82–83

1 Clinical trials are needed to establish safety, determine effectiveness as a treatment and to discover any side effects.

2 An experimental group of people is given the new treatment and a control group is given no treatment or a placebo. Participants are assigned randomly to each group to reduce bias.

3 A dummy treatment with no active ingredient.

4 The group size is made as large as possible.

5 If error bars between the two groups do not overlap, then there is a significant difference between the two groups.

6 Use a randomised, double blind trial. An experimental group is given the new treatment and a control group is given no treatment or a placebo. Participants are assigned **randomly** to each group to reduce bias in the distribution of characteristics (e.g. age and gender). In a **double-blind** study neither the investigator nor the participant is aware of the nature of the treatment the subject is receiving. The expectations of the researcher and the subject do not affect the outcome.

Revision questions, pp.84–85

1 a Synaptic vesicle.

b Vesicle moves to and fuses with pre-synaptic membrane. Neurotransmitter released into synaptic gap by exocytosis and diffuses across synaptic gap to bind with receptor on post-synaptic membrane.

c (i) Acetylcholine; (ii) It is broken down by enzymes and then reabsorbed into the pre-synaptic cell; (iii) Noradrenaline – removed intact before reabsorption into the pre-synaptic cell.

d Converging neural pathway.

e When the signal is weak, neurotransmitter from more than one pre-synaptic cell can combine to reach threshold in a process called summation.

f Axon.

g Glial cell.

h Slow down the speed of the nerve impulse.

i Antagonists prevent the neurotransmitter from binding to the receptor on the post-synaptic membrane.

j The number of receptors increases over time.

2 a Encoding.

b It is discarded.

c 7 ± 2

d Rehearsal.

e Chunking is where related items are grouped together to form fewer larger items.

ANSWERS (CONT)

f It is easier to remember items if you are in the same setting or context as when the memory was made.

3 a (i) Epithelial cells.

(ii) They produce secretions to trap dirt and pathogens.

b Histamine. It increases the permeability of capillaries and blood vessels to dilate, increasing blood flow to the site of infection.

c (i) Lysosomes contain digestive enzymes to break down pathogens;

(ii) Cytokines attract more phagocytes to the site of infection.

4 a Each lymphocyte has a single type of membrane receptor which is specific for one antigen. An antigen binds to its specific receptor on a lymphocyte. The specific lymphocyte undergoes repeated division, resulting in the formation of a clone of identical lymphocytes.

b (i) B-lymphocytes.

(ii) The body over reacts to an allergen (a harmless foreign substance). Histamine is produced resulting in inflammation and tissue damage.

c C

APPENDICES

INDEX

absent proteins 24
accuracy 9
acetylcholine 51, 69
acetylcholinesterase 71
achondroplasia 46
acoustic code 66
activation energy 30
addiction, recreational drugs 71
adenine (A) 14, 18, 19
adenosine diphosphate (ADP) 32, 33
adenosine triphosphate (ATP) 32, 33, 34
adjuvants 78, 79
ADP 32, 33
adrenalin 58
aerobic exercise 61
agonists 70, 71
AIDS 77
allergens 75
allergic asthma 75
allergic responses 75
allergy 75
Alzheimer's disease 70, 71
amino acids 22–3, 24, 25
amniocentesis 44, 45
anabolic reactions 28
anaphylactic shock 75
anomaly scans 44
antagonists 71
antenatal screening 44
antibodies 74–5, 76, 78, 79, 80
antibody-mediated immune response 74–5
antigenic variation 80–1
antigens 74–5, 76, 77, 78, 80–1
  types used in vaccines 78
apoptosis 76
archaeobiology 17
arteries 48, 50
arterioles 48
artificial insemination 42, 43
atheroma 54
atherosclerosis 54, 56, 59
ATP 32, 33, 34
atria 50
atrioventricular node (AVN) 51, 53
atrioventricular valves 50
autoimmune diseases 76
autonomic nervous system 51, 65
autosomal dominant inheritance 46

autosomal recessive inheritance 46
AVN (atrioventricular node) 51, 53
axon bulb 68
axons 68

B lymphocytes 74–5, 77, 79
basal metabolic rate (BMR) 61
biochemical testing 44
bioinformatics 26–7, 81
blastocysts 11, 41
blood glucose levels, regulation 58–9
blood pressure 52, 53
  in blood vessels 52
  in capillaries 48
  in heart 52
  in pregnancy 44
blood types, rhesus 44
blood vessels 48–9, 52
BMI 44, 60
BMR 61
body composition 60–1
body mass index (BMI) 44, 60
brain 64, 65, 66, 67

cancer cells 13
capillaries 48, 49
carbohydrates 58
cardiac cycle 50–1, 52
cardiac impulses 51
cardiac output 53
cardiovascular disease (CVD), pathology 54–7
cardiovascular system 48–9
  see also heart
catabolic reactions 28
cell-mediated immunity 74–5
cells
  auto-rhythmic 51
  body 68
  normal/healthy 13
  see also specific cells
cellular defence 74–7
cellular respiration 32–3
central nervous system (CNS) 64, 68
cerebellum 64
cerebral cortex 67, 70
cerebrum 64, 65
cholesterol 54, 56–7

INDEX

chorionic villus sampling 45
chromosome structure mutations 25
chromosomes 14
chunking 66
circulatory system 48–9
citrates 33
citric acid cycle 33
cleavage 41
clinical trials, vaccines and drugs
    82–3
clonal selection 74, 75, 76, 77
clones 74, 77
coagulation 72, 73
cocaine 71
codons 21
colour blindness 47
competitive inhibition 31
conducting system 51
contextual clues 67
contraception 42, 43
control experiment 9
cornea repair 12
coronary arteries 50
corpus callosum 64, 65
corpus luteum 40
Course Assessment 4
Course Assignment 4
creatine phosphate 34
cyanide 31
cystic fibrosis 46
cytokines 73, 76
cytosine (C) 14, 18, 19

data handling 8–9
dating scans 44
deep vein thrombosis (DVT) 55
dehydrogenase 33
deletion mutations 24, 25
dendrites 68
deoxyribonucleic acid see DNA
desensitisation 71
diabetes 58–9
  type 1 59, 78
  type 2 59, 60
diagnostic testing 44–5
diagnostics, DNA use in 17
diastole 50, 52, 53
diastolic pressure 52
differentiation 10, 41
DNA 14–15
  chromosomes 14
  coding regions see exons

comparison with mRNA 19
  non-coding regions see introns
  profiling 17
  replication 14–15
  sequencing 26, 27
DNA triplets 24
dopamine 13, 70, 71
double-blind studies 82
Down's syndrome 45
drug addiction 71
drug tolerance 71
dual coding 7
Duchenne muscular dystrophy 24, 47
duplication mutations 25
DVT 55

early embryo stem cells 11
ECGs 53
elaboration 67
electrocardiograms (ECGs) 53
electron transport chain 33
embolus 54
embryonic stem cells 11
encoding 66–7
end-product inhibition 31
endometrium 40, 41
endorphins 70
energy investment phase 32
energy pay-off phase 32
enzyme inhibitors 71
enzymes 30–1
  see also specific enzymes
epilepsy 65
epithelial cells 72
ethanol 71
ethical issues, stem cell use 12
exam hints 4
exercise 34–5, 57, 60, 61
  effects on body composition 61
exons 18, 20, 22
experimental design questions 9

FAD 33
FADH 33
family trees 46–7
fast-twitch muscle fibres 34, 35
fats 34, 56, 57, 60, 61
feedback inhibition 31
fertile period, determination 42
fertilisation 41
fertility 38, 40
fertility drugs 42

fibrin 54, 55
fibrinogen 54
fibrous proteins 23
fields of view 65
flash cards 6
fluorescent labelling 27
follicle stimulating hormone (FSH) 39, 40
follicular cells 40
follicular phase 40, 41
frame-shift mutations 24
fructose 39
FSH 39, 40

gametes 38
gene expression 18–19, 21
gene probes 27
gene sequences 26–7
genes
    regulating expression 29
    switching on and off 28–9
genetic codes 14
genetic counsellors 44, 46
genetic disorders 24
genome (human) 26–7
genomics 26–7
germline cells 10, 38
glial cells 69
globular proteins 23
glucagon 58
glucose 58–9
glucose tolerance tests 59
glycogen 34
glycolysis 32, 33
Graafian follicle 40
guanine (G) 14, 18, 19

haemophilia 47
hay fever 75
HDL 56–7
heart 11, 48, 50–1
    blood pressure in 52
    cardiac cycle 50–1, 52
    cardiac output 53
    components 50
heart attack 54
heart rate 51, 53
herd immunity 78–9, 80
herd immunity threshold 78, 79, 80
high-density lipoproteins (HDL) 56–7
histamine 72, 73
HIV 77, 79
hormones 39

see also specific hormones
human genome sequence 26–7
human immunodeficiency virus (HIV) 77, 79
Huntington's chorea 46
hydrogen bonds 20, 23
hyperglycemia 58
hypertension 52, 53
hypothalamus 64

ICSH 39
ICSI 43
immune response 74–5
immune system 72, 76, 80
    direct attack on 77
immunisation 78–81
immunity 72, 74–5, 76, 78–9, 80
immunological memory 77
immunology 72–3
implantation 41, 42
in vitro fertilisation (IVF) 42, 43, 45
incomplete dominance inheritance 47
induced fit 30
infectious diseases 78, 80
infertility 42–3
inflammatory response 72, 73
influenza 80–1
inheritance 46–7
inhibition 31
inhibitors 71
insertion mutations 24
insulin 58, 59
inter neurons 68
interleaving 7
interstitial cell stimulating hormone
        (ICSH) 39
interstitial cells 38, 39
intracytoplasmic sperm injection (ICSI) 43
introns 18, 20, 22
inversion mutations 25
irreversible reactions 28
IVF 42, 43, 45

karotyping 45
kidneys, disease 59

lactate metabolism 33, 34
LDL 56–7
LH 40
limbic system 64, 67
lipoproteins 56–7
liver 58
long-term memory 66, 67

low-density lipoproteins (LDL) 56–7
luteal phase 40, 41
luteinising hormone (LH) 40
lymphatic system 49
lymphocytes 74–5, 76–7, 78, 79
lysozyme 72

macrovascular disease 59
mast cells 72, 73
medulla oblongata 51, 64
meiosis 10, 14
memory 66–7
memory cells 77, 78, 80
menstrual cycle 40–1, 42
messenger RNA (mRNA) 19, 20, 21, 22
metabolism 28–9
mind maps 6
missense mutations 24
mitochondria 32, 34
mitosis 10, 14
motor neurons 68
mRNA 19, 20, 21, 22
multiple sclerosis 76
multipotency 10, 11
muscle fatigue 34
muscle fibres, skeletal 34–5
mutations 24–5
myelination 69
myocardial infarction (MI) 54
myoglobin 34

NAD 32, 33
NADH 32, 33
natural killer cells 73
negative feedback 39
nerve cells 68
nervous system 64–5, 68–9
neural pathways 69
neurons 68
neurotransmitters 70–1
    see also acetylcholine;
        noradrenaline
nicotine 71
non-competitive inhibition 31
nonsense mutations 24
noradrenaline (nor-epinephrine) 51, 69
nuchal translucency (NT) scans 45
nucleotides 14

obesity 60–1
    and atherosclerosis 54
    and cholesterol levels 57

oestrogen 40, 41
ovaries, changes during menstrual cycle 40
oviduct 41
ovulation 40, 42
oxygen debt 34

P wave 53
pancreas 59
parasympathetic division 65
parasympathetic nerves 51, 65
Parkinson's disease 13, 70
past-paper practice 6–7
pathogens 72–9, 80, 82
PCR 16–17
pedigree charts 46–7
percent change 8
peripheral nerves, damage 59
peripheral nervous system 64, 65
peripheral vascular disorders 54–5
personalised medicine 27
PGD 45
phagocytes 72, 73, 77
phagocytosis 73
pharmacogenetics 27
phenotypes 23
phenylketonuria (PKU) 45, 46
phosphofructokinase 32
phylogenetics 17
pituitary gland 39, 40, 41, 64
PKU 45, 46
placebos 82
plaque 54
plasmin 55
plasminogen 55
plasticity 69
pluripotency 10, 11
point mutations 24
polygenic inheritance 47
polymerase 15, 16, 17, 20
polymerase chain reaction (PCR) 16–17
polypeptides 22–3
post-synaptic membrane 68
postnatal screening 45
pre-implantation genetic diagnosis
    (PGD) 45
pre-synaptic membrane 68
pregnancy, problems during 44
primers 16
progesterone 40, 41
prostaglandins 39
prostrate gland 38, 39
protein synthesis 20–1

proteins 22–3, 24, 25
  see also specific proteins
prothrombrin 54
puberty 39, 40
pulmonary embolism 55

QRS complex 53
Question Papers 4

randomisation 82
rehearsal 66–7
reliability 9
reproductive systems 38–9, 40–1
respiration 32–3
respiratory substrates 32
retina, damage 59
Retinitis Pigmentosa 26
retrieval practice 6
reversible reactions 28
revision techniques 6–7
revision tips 4–5
reward pathway 70
rheumatoid arthritis 78
ribonucleic acid *see* RNA
ribosomal RNA (rRNA) 19
ribosomes 18, 19, 21
RNA 18–19
  splicing 20, 22
  see also messenger RNA (mRNA);
      ribosomal RNA (rRNA);
      transfer RNA (tRNA)
rRNA 19

SAN (sinoatrial node) 51, 53
scans 44–5
schizophrenia 70, 71
screening
  antenatal 44
  postnatal 45
self-renewal 10, 11
semen 39
semilunar valves 50
seminal vesicles 38, 39
seminiferous tubules 38, 39
sensitisation 71
sensory memory 66
sensory neurons 68
serial position effect 66–7
sex-linked inheritance 46–7
short-term memory 66–7
sickle-cell disease 24, 47
single-base mutations 24

sinoatrial node (SAN) 51, 53
skeletal muscle fibres 34–5
skin grafts 12
slow-twitch muscle fibres 34, 35
smoking 57
somatic cells 10
somatic nervous system 65
spaced practice 7
specialised cells 10
sperm 42, 43
  production 38, 39
sperm cells 38
sphygmomanometers 52
splice site mutations 24
splicing 20, 22
statins 57
stem cells 11, 12–13
strands (DNA) 20
  anti-parallel 14
  coding 20
  lagging 15
  leading 15
strands (mRNA) 20, 21
streptokinase 55
stroke 54
stroke volume 53
substitution mutations 24
substrate concentration, effect on rate of reaction 30,
  31
substrates, respiratory 32
summation 69
sympathetic division 65
sympathetic nerves 51, 65
synapses 68–9
synaptic cleft 68
synaptic vesicles 68
systole 50, 52, 53
systolic pressure 52

T-cell receptors (TCR) 76
T lymphocytes (cells) 76–7, 78
T wave 53
Tay-Sachs syndrome 24
TCR 76
testes 38
testosterone 38, 39, 42
thrombin 54
thrombolytic medications 55
thrombosis 54–5
thymine (T) 14, 18, 19
tissue plasminogen activator 55
tissue stem cells 11

transcription 18–19, 20
transfer RNA (tRNA) 19, 21
transition state 30
translation 21
translocation mutations 25
tRNA 19, 21
tuberculosis (TB) 77

ultrasound imaging 44
uracil 19
uterus, changes during menstrual cycle 40–1

vaccination 78, 79, 80

vaccine clinical trials 82–3
vacuoles 73
variables 9
vasodilation 72, 73
veins 48, 49
ventricles 50
venules 48
visual code 66

white blood cells 72, 73, 74

zygote 10, 41